The
Perfum
guide

The Perfume guide

Susan Irvine

Haldane Mason

Dedication
For my sister, Karenina, and her sillage of Arpège

Acknowledgements

The author and publisher would like to thank all the public relations executives at the
many perfume houses who helped in gathering information for this book. Thanks also to Fleur
Clackson and Naomi Waters for their thorough research, to perfumer Lyn Harris for her help in com-
piling the glossary, and special thanks to Jean Coppendale for pulling everything together.

First published in the UK in 2000 by
Haldane Mason Ltd
59 Chepstow Road
London W2 5BP

ISBN: 1-902463-15-3

A HALDANE MASON BOOK
Art Director: Ron Samuel
Editorial Director: Sydney Francis
Editors: Jo-Anne Cox, Jean Coppendale
Designers: Zoë Mellors, Maria Pritchard
Perfume Researchers: Fleur Clackson, Naomi Waters
Photography: Joff Lee

Colour reproduction by CK Litho Ltd, UK

Printed in the UAE

Contents

Introduction   6

Floral Family   20

Fruity Family   68

Herbaceous Family   86

Chypre Family   100

Oriental Family   116

Mail order and
    stockists   141

Index   142

Introduction

Why wear perfume?

Helen Keller, who was blind, deaf and dumb, wrote: 'In the odour of young men there is something elemental, as of fire, storm and salt sea. It pulsates with buoyancy and desire. It suggests all the things strong and beautiful and joyous and gives me a sense of physical happiness.'

   Why cover that up? I doubt that we would if we could smell this natural bouquet as vividly as she could. But few of us have such an enhanced sense of smell. What seems, unfortunately, to be rather more penetrating is the odour of bodies when they are not signalling 'fire, storm and salt sea' but, instead, their urgent need to shower.

   In previous centuries, one reason fragrance was liberally used was indeed to mask the odour of unwashed bodies and clothes. This is no longer true. Today, we wash regularly and a morning spritz of scent is, for many of us, a final signal to ourselves and others that our bodies are clean, fresh and, therefore, attractive. Even then it's a highly individual thing. The first scent you should be conscious of, and love, is your body's own. Beyond that, wearing scent is a way of developing that under-used route to pleasure: the nose.

Scent and sex

Used judiciously, perfumes don't mask – they enhance the natural allure of our body-scent.

Scent can be a potent seducer and one that works on a very fundamental level. Movie star Joan Crawford was wearing Youth Dew when she met her husband, Alfred Steele. 'I can't stop dancing with you,' he said. 'You smell so exquisite.' The French writer Flaubert kept his mistress's scented mittens in a drawer and was intoxicated by their smell. And in *Faust*, Goethe wrote that Paris drove the Trojan palace women mad with desire by his 'perfume of incense and roses mixed' with 'fresh living blood'.

Scent ingredients such as musk, castoreum, ambergris and civet, which derive from animals or synthetics modelled on animal odours, are akin to the body's own aroma – musk especially. By applying a fragrance which contains one of these ingredients, we intensify our body's sexual signals. By blending them with flowers and plant essences, we enrich the message, adding elements which, while they may not smell like us, are beautiful in their own right.

Some flowers, like jasmine and orange flower, also contain scent-chemicals which

Orange flower

are close to those released naturally by our own bodies.

During the puritanical nineteenth century, this sexual aspect of perfume gave it a bad name. 'Misuse of perfumes gives birth to all kinds of neuroses,' wrote Dr Rostand in 1826. 'Hysteria, hypochondria and melancholia are its most usual effects.' The entranced expression on the face of a woman smelling a flower was even likened to her expression when making love, leading some experts to warn that the dark relationship between woman and flowers could lead to orgasm.

Chanel No5, a classic of the twentieth century

Mood-altering aromas

Attracting the opposite sex is an age-old reason for wearing fragrance. But nowadays we have rediscovered an equally compelling reason: the ability of odours to affect mood.

Choosing a perfume because of how it affects your mood makes sense. You might choose a light, energizing fragrance when you are setting off to work, and a richer, more mellow fragrance for the evening. You might spritz on your favourite lavender-based scent when you need calming. Or choose a scent that you find comforting, such as one based on rose and vanilla, if you feel vulnerable.

But research into how scent affects mood has led to one key rule. Your individual history with an odour overrides its generally perceived effect. This is due to the connection between odour and memory. For example, if you have good memories of the jasmine scent your mother wore, chances are that, whenever you smell jasmine, it will make you feel good. But if you smelt jasmine while going through a traumatic experience, you may feel uneasy around its scent even years later, without consciously knowing why.

Some aromas nevertheless have a broad appeal. Vanilla, for example, is almost universally attractive, perhaps because it rcminds us of the security of babyhood. Baby powder is vanilla-scented and one hypothesis speculates that a mother's milk may contain chemicals similar to vanilla, so that we feel contented and safe whenever we smell it. It is because certain odours have such wide acceptance that we find them in so many perfumes. There is a belief in fragrance marketing that a successful perfume should be based on a core of familiar, well-loved ingredients – such as roses, jasmine and vanilla – with the twist of something new in the top notes. Many of today's perfume launches follow this formula.

Self-expression

Above all, we wear scent to express ourselves. Fragrance is a language we can learn to use.

Traditionally, women sought the one perfume that they felt expressed them like a signature and wore it for life. There is something intensely romantic about this. Because of the way smell uniquely accesses memory in the brain, those who know you will automatically think of you when they smell that scent. But you can, of course, have a whole wardrobe of fragrances. Because your sense of smell is so individual, only you can decide which ones are right for you. This guide aims to help you track them down.

Jasmine

Choosing a perfume

Finding a fragrance can be bewildering when there is so little guidance in department stores and perfumeries.

In stores, fragrances are grouped according to the house that markets them. If you like a fragrance by one house, there's usually no method to help you find similar scents to compare it with. Meanwhile, a hundred or so new perfumes appear every year, although only about ten of these survive.

Guy Laroche

Fidji, a light, green floral perfume

There are no golden rules about which perfumes are right for whom. But there are several theories. The best-known theory is that your skin or hair colouring establishes the range of scents you should choose from, so that blonde women should choose lighter citrus or floral fragrances while dark-haired women should go for heavier chypres and orientals.

Generally, I don't hold with this view. I have known blonde women who suited orientals and African women who smelt wonderful in eaux de Colognes. Red heads are an exception as they often have a more acidic skin mantle which alters a perfume's aroma. Subtle differences in skin acidity is one reason why scents smell different on different people. But there are other factors such as diet, hormones and the strength of your natural smell. In the end, it's purely personal choice.

How to choose a scent

1 **Don't choose your fragrance because it smells good on someone else.** It may not smell the same on you.

2 **Don't smell it in the bottle.** If you do, you are smelling mostly the top notes and the alcohol it is diluted in. This also gives no idea of how it will smell on your skin. Think of your skin as the final, essential ingredient in a fragrance.

3 **Don't decide in the first minute.** Fragrance notes evaporate at different rates and over the first ten minutes especially, a scent changes several times. You may love the top notes, which are first to be smelt, but it's the base notes you will live with for most of the day. The final character may take an hour to develop.

4 **Don't smell too many fragrances at one go.** As a rough rule, four or five are usually adequate. Sometimes, 'cleaning your palette' by whisking coffee beans under your nose can refresh its powers.

5 **Different strengths of the same perfume smell different.** It's not just that eau de parfum contains more oils than eau de toilette, but that perfumers formulate the eau de toilette with more top notes. The pure parfum will have different ingredients highlighted as well.

6 **Consider pure parfum as an option.** It's not as fashionable as eau de toilette or eau de parfum, the 'lighter' concentrations with more alcohol. But while pure parfum is more expensive, you use much less (you don't spray it). It's often the most masterfully blended.

7 **Ignore sexual divisions.** Most women are not inhibited about this and wear men's colognes at will. But men too – irrespective of sexual orientation – can smell sexy in a 'woman's' fragrance.

8 **Don't be prejudiced.** If everyone tells you, for example, that Poison is too vulgar, too '1980s', just go and smell it. It might be right for you.

Simple rules for wearing scent

1 Less is more. Aim to leave a lingering sillage, not announce your arrival with an olfactory trumpet blast. 'Sillage' is a French term for the faint trail of scent left behind a woman when she leaves a room. Very mysterious, very Catherine Deneuve. Many modern scent-lovers get it the other way round and wear so much it enters a room before they do. Remember, the longer you wear a scent, the less you smell it. While for others, it's still strong.

2 Less is sexier. Scent is about intimacy. It's more alluring for someone to just catch a whiff of your scent when you give them a social 'hello' kiss, or when they lean forward to hear what you are saying. No one should ever smell your scent before they can see the colour of your eyes.

3 Put it anywhere. Putting scent on the traditional pulse points – behind ears, on throat, wrists and inner elbow – makes no difference to how quickly it is diffused. But somehow they are nice places to put it. Also try between the breasts or behind your knees (which is particularly good for creating 'sillage'). Some women spray perfume in the air, then walk into the mist. This gives a light, all-over scent. The best advice was Chanel's. She said put scent wherever you want to be kissed.

4 If your skin is allergic to perfume try the old-fashioned method: tucking a scent-sprayed cotton ball into your bra. Or spray a little scent in your hair.

5 If you think you don't like perfume – experiment. Some people find perfumes too 'perfume-y' or cloying. Seek out the small houses, which I have made a point of including in this book. Many do simpler, cleaner scents quite unlike the more mainstream houses. Try some of the popular new 'eaux' which come only in eau de toilette strength. Use only the bath oil or body lotion in a fragrance line. These should scent your body long after the bath, but delicately. Blend your own from essential oils. But remember the first rule of perfumery: proportion is everything.

6 Storing scent. Marilyn Monroe kept her knickers in the fridge and wore nothing but Chanel No5 in bed. She might have been better off keeping her knickers on in bed and putting her Chanel No5 in the fridge. Heat and light deteriorate perfume. If you keep it in the fridge it will last for years. A hot, sunlit bathroom is the worst place for it. Also, the more air gets into the bottle, the more it oxidizes. Some change perceptibly in a year, some in three. Use it often and always replace the stopper.

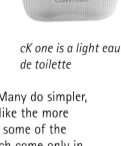

cK one is a light eau de toilette

The wrist is a pulse point, a traditional place to put scent

How to use this book

This book aims to help you cut a path through the fragrance jungle whether you are choosing for yourself, for a friend or for a partner.

The guide

There are over 200 fragrances listed in this guide. I have included a balance of great classics, recent launches, popular scents and also scents from small houses that are worth discovering.

The families

Scents are divided into families, the traditional way to categorize fragrances. There is no authorized way to divide the fragrances or even choose the families; different authors and perfume manufacturers do it slightly differently. The key families in most systems, however, have always been floral, oriental and chypre. I have kept these.

Traditionally, the fourth category was the 'fougère' or 'ferny' category. Ferns themselves have no scent, and this was a 'fantasy' note mostly based on lavender. There are few women's perfumes available nowadays that fall into this category, but many modern scents have a cool herbal character that would include lavender. I have grouped these into a 'herbaceous' category. Finally, I have included a fruity family. Fruit-dominated notes, apart from the citrusy eaux de Colognes, are a relatively recent phenomenon so this is a new category.

The main characteristic of each family is explained at the opening of its chapter.

Within the families

Each chapter is further sub-divided. Each family opens with the lightest, freshest version of the family, and gradually works through to the richest or heaviest version. These sub-sections are given in the running heads. For example:

Floral family

Green Florals: flower-based scents with a sap or grassy note

Fresh Florals: lightly floral, not too sweet

Aqueous Florals: a new group with an emollient, 'watery' note

Fresh Fruity Florals: light florals with a distinctive fruit note

Powdery Florals: with the dryness of powder

Woody Florals: with a distinctive woodiness, and sometimes spiciness, in the base notes

Aldehydic Florals: in the family launched by Chanel No5; characterized by a sparkle that makes them fly off the skin

Pure Florals: sometimes single flower notes, sometimes bouquets; other ingredients faint or not present

Sweet Florals: notable for sweetness and creaminess

Rich Florals: deeper than sweet florals, these florals have a high proportion of base notes, perhaps vanilla or musk

Finding a perfume-path

Often, people are attracted to a type of scent. It may be they tend to return to fresh florals. It may be that they like the denser and animal base notes of the oriental family. This is where grouping perfumes into the families is useful.

If you like AnaïsAnaïs, for example, look at the scents in the same sub-section of Fresh Florals. Or it may be that you like a rich floral like Escada or Arden's Fifth Avenue. Look at the other rich florals and into the sweet floral category just above it. As the preponderance of base notes in rich florals is also a characteristic of the

oriental family, look at these too, especially the floral orientals, as you already know you like floral scents.

As these examples show, there are several paths to follow from one 'starter' fragrance.

a) look at the others in the sub-section of the family where your starter scent is located. Look also at the sub-section just above or just below it.

b) look at the other key-words in the sub-section name. If it is an aqueous floral, look for 'aqueous' in the other families, as you may well like these.

c) a quick glance will show you whether your starter scent is at the beginning or the end of a family. If it's at the beginning, it's lighter; if it's at the end, it's heavier. Cross-reference with the light or heavy end of the other families as well. Note too that herbaceous scents as a family are light. Orientals and chypres as families are richer.

These methods provide a structured route through the fragrance world. As you follow the path you cut out for yourself, you will learn more about scent, and also more about what you like, circling in ever closer on scents that are right for you. Remember that while this book serves as a guide, highlighting links between scents, only you can finally choose the scent that you like.

If you like L'Eau d'Issey look in the aqueous floral section

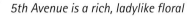

5th Avenue is a rich, ladylike floral

What each entry tells you

Each fragrance is given half a page description, unless it is a classic, where it is given a whole page.

Perfume house

You will find the name of the house – be it fashion designer, perfume house or even celebrity – under whose name the fragrance is marketed. Except in a very few cases such as Chanel and Guerlain, there is no in-house perfumer at these houses making the scent. Instead, the house puts out a brief of the kind of scent they are looking for to several fragrance manufacturing companies. Perfumers at these companies will work in great secrecy, in competition against each other, to try and create the winning fragrance.

Perfumer

You will also find the name of the perfumer who created the scent. This information is not normally available to the public but it can be a useful method of tracking scents. The same perfumer may create fragrances for rival houses. Perfumers often have a 'signature' that makes their scents recognizable. It may be that what you love is this signature. If you like Saint Laurent's Paris, knowing it was created by Sophia Grojsman might lead you to try Trésor. Even though one is a pure floral and the other a fresh, fruity floral, they have the perfumer's signature in common. Sometimes a house will not release the perfumer's name or it is simply not available; these entries are marked 'unknown'. For other entries, only the perfume manufacturing company is known, for example, IFF (International Flavours & Fragrances), Givaudan Roure, Quest, Dragoco, Robertet.

Date

This is the date of the fragrance's first launch anywhere in the world.

How it smells

In each entry there is a two-pronged approach to conveying how a fragrance smells. One is the list of top, middle and base notes (see 'How a Fragrance is Constructed'). Only the most discernible notes have been included; some fragrances contain many more notes than listed.

Nowadays, many synthetics are included in perfumes. Some of these synthetics are beautiful aroma-chemicals, costing as much as, if not more than, natural ones. Many more, however, are poor versions of nature's original, chosen because they are cheaper. Other synthetics clone smells which cannot be extracted from the natural source, for example, gardenia or peach. Most animal notes today such as musk and ambergris are synthetic copies ensuring that no animal is killed to extract it.

When a note is listed as, for example, rose, peach or musk, it refers to the aroma and not the origin, natural or otherwise, of the aroma.

I have listed the most noticeable note first in each section of top, middle or base notes. Knowing what is in your fragrance is useful, but beware. The first rule of perfumery is proportion. You can mix lemon, rose, jasmine and musk a hundred

Obsession is an oriental, rich in base notes

different ways, all in slightly different proportions and they will smell a bit different. The ideal method, therefore, is to look at the notes in conjunction with the character assessment.

In the 'character' section I give my assessment of how the fragrance smells. Often I follow the development of the ingredients; this will allow you more insight into how the top, middle and base notes actually unfold. For example, if you look at the 'character' of the famous perfume Joy, by Jean Patou, I explain that it is almost nothing but the smell of the finest rose and jasmine together. This is more helpful than reading the notes alone.

Sometimes I give a personal assessment which you may well not agree with. This is no bad thing — it's just my opinion. Smell it for yourself and then decide.

The story

Some scents have wonderful stories attached to them, like Chanel No5, Bandit or Arpège. One of the purposes of this guide is to acquaint you with the stories behind the scents, and to provide a little more information about the house.

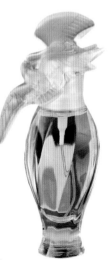

L'Air du Temps in a flacon originally designed by Lalique

How a perfume is constructed

We smell the essential oils and chemicals in a perfume as they evaporate. Not everything in a perfume evaporates at once. The smaller, more volatile chemicals evaporate first; these are 'green' notes like galbanum, citrus oils and many fruit notes, lavender and pine. Because these are the first notes we smell they are called 'top notes'.

Next the mid-notes or heart notes take off; these are generally the flowers and sometimes the lighter spices and woods. Finally, the base notes, also known as the 'drydown', become preponderant. These are heavier molecules such as amber, musk, tonka bean, sandalwood, patchouli and resins like benzoin and styrax.

Some molecules of all the ingredients evaporate all the time. But the top notes are up and gone in two to twenty minutes. Once they have mostly disappeared, we become more aware of the heart notes. After half an hour to an hour, when they are mainly gone, it is the base notes which become distinctive as these are generally what are left. Base notes can linger overnight. Chypre and oriental fragrances are so rich in base notes that these are clearly discernible from the beginning.

A well-constructed fragrance has harmony and smoothness. Top notes blend into heart notes, which, in turn, blend into base notes, as they would in a musical symphony. The overall composition of a fragrance and the proportion of each ingredient can affect the rate of evaporation of each note, so some wood notes, for example, might be listed as heart notes or base notes – depending on when they become most detectable.

Eau de Colognes contain 3-5 per cent perfume oils

An 'accord' in fragrance is a term parallel to a chord in music. It is a group of two or more ingredients which meld together with more harmony than usual, often giving a new odour that seems more than the sum of its parts (see glossary).

Traditional fragrances change over time; this unfolding is part of their great appeal. However, in the last fifteen years or so, there has been a trend for 'horizontal' perfumes which smell pretty much the same at the end as at the beginning. Usually these have a 'twist' of top notes that die away quickly to leave a central note which endures longer than usual with little change.

Which concentration?

Until the 1950s, perfumes only existed as 'extraits' or pure parfums. If you wanted a lighter splash, you bought an eau de toilette or an eau de Cologne, which smelt totally different. Then Patou had the idea of doing a lighter, cheaper version of Joy with less perfume oils. Nowadays, many perfumes come in two or three strengths.

An 'extrait' or pure 'parfum' has the highest concentration of fragrance oils in alcohol, typically 15 to 40 per cent. Anything more diluted is classified as an 'eau' or water, and in fact, contains a certain amount of distilled water mixed with the alcohol. An eau de parfum contains typically 10 to 20 per cent of fragrance. An eau de toilette: 8 to 10 per cent. An eau de Cologne: 3 to 5 per cent. An eau fraîche: about 3 per cent.

Glossary of unfamiliar ingredients and terms

Accord: a term used to denote a harmonious blend of several ingredients that echo one another. The major accord in a fragrance sets its character. For example the orris–oakmoss–galbanum accord is the heart of Chanel No19 while Shalimar's theme is a classic oriental accord: heliotrope-benzoin-labdanum-patchouli-musk.

Aldehydes: bring strength and vibrancy to a fragrance, bursting open the flower notes. Aldehydes are an aroma-chemical family first used in large doses in Chanel No5. As well as bringing diffusion, they each have a distinctive aroma. C8 has lemon undertones, C9 has a rosy note.

Amber: a term used to describe a base note in perfumery that is warm, erotic, animalic with a leather tone.

Ambergris: very subtle note, animalic with a tang of the sea and moss. From an intestinal deposit of the sperm whale; rarely used.

Ambrette seeds: peachy with musky undertones. From the seeds of the ambrette plant.

Balsam of Peru: vanilla-like smell with a pungent clove note. A tree resin.

Balsams: a family of ingredients that smell dense with a vanilla-like suaveness and a spicy note, different with each balsam. They also sometimes have a cool, resinous edge. From resins exuded by various trees.

Frankincense is the typical balsam.

Base: a perfumer's personal interpretation of a theme or note. For example, the jasmine base a perfumer uses will be her 'signature' version, set off with other ingredients to emphasize the aspects of jasmine she loves.

Benzoin: nutty, caramel smell. A little spicy, balsamic. A tree resin.

Bergamot: fresh, herbaceous lemon-orange smell, also used in Earl Grey tea. From the peel of the fruit of the bergamot tree, native to southern Italy.

Bigarade orange: bitter orange oil, expressed from the peel of the bigarade or Seville orange tree. The bigarade orange tree is known as 'the pig of perfumery' as it yields so many scent ingredients.

Boronia: fruity violet note. Beautiful; rare. From the *Boronia megastigma*, an Australian shrub.

Cashmeran or cashmerande or cashmere woods: a velvety amber odour, very refined. 'Cashmere woods' has an additional woody accent. Example of a beautiful synthetic.

Cassis/blackcurrant buds: cassis is a synthetically-created berry base; tangy and can be cloying. Popular because it is tenacious, so is much used in American perfumery. Blackcurrant buds: a greener, lighter version with a touch of cat.

Castoreum: warm, sweet, animalic and stinky. Like civet, adds a fleshy warmth and eroticism to a fragrance in small doses. It is a secretion from the genital scent sacs of the castor beaver. Synthetics are now often substituted.

Cedar/Virginia cedar: cedar from the Atlas mountains is intensely woody, with a narcotic, deep incense background. Virginia cedar is sweeter, less intense.

Centifolia rose or rose de mai: lemony, crystal-clear rose, with a geranium note. This type of rose is famously grown in Grasse (though only a few fields now) where it is called rose de mai or May rose. Also grown in Morocco.

Civet: musky, fresh sweat note. In the raw, smells like a sewer, but dropped in minute proportion into a floral bouquet, it metamorphoses, adding radiant heat and sexiness. Extracted from the anal glands of the civet cat; exported from Ethiopia. Very good synthetic copies are often used.

Coumarin: a very important aroma-chemical – see also tonka bean. Haylike, with a coconuty undertow.

Damascene rose: honey-sweet and more spicy and velvety than the centifolia rose. Grown in Bulgaria and Turkey.

Drydown: the final characteristic of a fragrance; usually occurs after an hour. You must be comfortable with a scent's drydown as it's what you live with.

Galbanum: the classic leafy green note. Perfume guru Arctander says it's 'like green peppers or tossed green salad'. Full of fresh air, quite sharp and a little minty. Exuded from the branches of an Iranian shrub.

Headspace or Living Flower Technology: a technique used to capture the aroma given off by a growing plant. The scented air is analysed using gas chromatography which gives a breakdown of the flower's chemical composition. Attempts are then made to reproduce this in the lab. The idea is to capture something closer to the smell of the living plant than the essential oil extracted from it, which alters due to the heat used in processing. Tremendous learning tool, but results are mixed. The prefix 'Living' to an ingredient, e.g., 'Living osmanthus' means it was created using this method.

Hedione: like jasmine without the clotted cream density. Perfumer Lyn Harris calls it transparent jasmine and says it gives fizz to citrus notes 'a bit like chamapagne'. First used in Eau Sauvage.

Incense or frankincense or olibanum: all one and the same. The classic church incense smell with its almost medicinal topnote and erotic undertow.

Labdanum: sexy, rich, animalic scent with a leather undertone that goes well with oakmoss. Exuded from the shrub rock rose that grows all round the Mediterranean Sea.

Linalool: sweet, silken, calming, floral scent. Rosy and herbaceous, but with a slight bitter edge. From rosewood. Also found in coriander, lavender and lavandin.

Neroli: fresh and light flower smell with a hint of orange, the classic floral note in eaux de Colognes such as 4711. Like orange blossom, neroli comes from the flower of the bitter orange tree but is extracted in a different way which gives a different smell.

Oakmoss: sea-like; creamy, damp and very sensual. Extracted from a lichen.

Opopanax: smoky, oriental spicy note with undertones of celery and fennel. Used in mossy, forest accords and oriental bases. A tree resin.

Orange flower or orange blossom: rich, sweet flowers on the level of jasmine and tuberose. Extracted from the blossom of the bitter or Seville orange tree. Known as 'the queen of the orange tree'.

Orris: buttery, velvety richness with fruity undertone; often chocolaty and carroty. Like something half-flesh, half-flower; orris brings voluptuous depth. Extracted from the rhizome of the iris root. The best is the Florence iris. The rhizomes are stored for two years before being processed. Often used in chypre and oriental fragrances.

Osmanthus: apricoty scent; expensive and rare. From the blossom of trees native to China and Japan.

Palmarosa: fresh, rosy, herbaceous smell, with marked geranium note.

Extracted from an Indian grass.

Petitgrain: woody, herbaceous with floral and orangey note. Extracted from twigs and leaves of the bitter orange tree.

Sillage: a French term for a lingering trail of scent. When you wear a fragrance this is what you leave behind.

Styrax: weird. A resin that smells like plastic glue with a cinnamon edge.

Tolu Balsam: like cinnamon vanilla. A tree resin.

Tonka bean: balsamic, hay-like with an overall vanilla tone and a touch of almond. The seed from a West African tree, it contains up to 40 per cent of coumarin, which is the smell of new-mown hay.

Tree moss: delicately sensual, dusty, earthy aroma. Extracted from a lichen.

Vetiver: rich, dry, earthy and rough – a dark green undergrowth smell. Wonderful in hot weather. From the root of a grass that grows wild in Ceylon, India, Burma. The best comes from Java.

Wormwood or artemisia: powerful, camphor-like smell, green and bittersweet. The heart of it is close to sage and rosemary. The drydown is tea-like. A herb.

Ylang-ylang: sensual, sweet, exotic flower of the *Cananga odorata*, somewhat like jasmine (but much cheaper). A love-hate smell. 'Big' florals usually have a high proportion. Grown in Madagascar.

The
floral

Family

Chapter 1

When we think of a fragrance, we imagine a bunch
of flowers, distilled. Florals is the largest fragrance
family and there are two main types, scents
dominated by a single flower note, such as Diorissimo
(lily of the valley) and those based on a bouquet of
many flowers, such as AnaïsAnaïs. Some also contain
a green or fresh note to give them a more airy feel
(if you like these, look also at the Herbaceous family).
Others have fruity accents (if you like these look at the
mid-section of the Fruity family). At the other end of
the spectrum are scents thick as clotted cream, full
of rich flowers like ylang-ylang, jasmine and tuberose
or with more base notes such as vanilla and musk.
These tend towards the floral orientals.

Vent Vert

Character

In *Perfume Legends* Michael Edwards writes of Vent Vert: 'Sharp and fresh as cut grass, it exploded with the green scent of galbanum, an oil extracted from . . . an Iranian grass . . . but Vent Vert's accord proved too extreme to be popular'. The relaunch of this great classic fragrance in 1991 saw it becoming more floral, less bright green.

Story

Vent Vert or 'green wind' (it sounds much better in French) is a blast of plant life. It was the first real 'green' fragrance created by a brilliant woman perfumer, Germaine Cellier, one of the very few in her time. She also created the cult scents Fracas and Bandit for Piguet (see p. 59 and p. 114) and Jolie Madame for Balmain (see p. 113).

Top notes
Lemon, bergamot, sweet lime, galbanum, basil, neroli, marigold
Middle notes
Lily of the valley, rose, violet, jasmine, sage
Base notes
Sandalwood, musk, oakmoss

House	Pierre Balmain
Date	1945
Perfumer	Germaine Cellier

Fidji

Top notes
Galbanum, bergamot
Middle notes
Bulgarian rose, ylang-ylang, clove, jasmine, tuberose, orris
Base notes
Amber, balsam, musk, patchouli, sandalwood

House	Guy Laroche
Date	1966
Perfumer	Josephine Catapano

Character

A fresh green floral, breezy yet fairly sweet, which becomes more erotic and enigmatically woody in the base notes.

Story

With the youth and feminist revolutions of the 1960s, young women no longer wanted to imitate the grown-up, groomed look of their mothers. They wanted to be rebels. Rebels do not wear perfume, especially not the feminine chypres that dominated the 1950s. Several companies tried to lure young women with fragrances, but it was Fidji that finally did it – not only because of its youthful green-floral feel, but also because it was brilliantly marketed. Fiji is a group of South Sea islands, and the name conjured up exotic travel at a time when jetting off on a plane was still the height of glamour. The ad-line too was inspired with its new play on the old 'woman-mystery-perfume' link: 'A woman is an island. Fidji is her perfume.'

Safari

Character

A beautifully composed floral with a true green top note that smells like freshly cut, wet grass. This fades into flowers that seem light and alive. The jasmine is Italian, the fruitiest of all jasmines. There's a tribute to Roudnitska's Diorella in the heart note; then a powdery, woody drydown. If you like the light florals of the late 1990s, but find them lacking in personality, look no further.

Story

Safari is the Swahili word for journey and the scent was inspired by pictures taken by Ralph Lauren's wife, Ricky, on a journey to Kenya. The cut-glass bottle comes from a Victorian piece in Ralph Lauren's collection.

Top notes	
Galbanum, orange, narcissus, marigold, hyacinth, aldehydes	
Middle notes	
Rose de mai, jasmine, orange flower, broom, carnation, orris	
Base notes	
Cedar, vetiver, sandalwood, patchouli, amber, moss	

House	Ralph Lauren
Date	1990
Perfumer	Dominique Ropion

Eternity

Top notes	
Freesia, mandarin, sage, narcissus, lily, leafy note	
Middle notes	
Lily of the valley, marigold, apricot, peach	
Base notes	
Patchouli, sandalwood	

House	Calvin Klein
Date	1988
Perfumer	Sophia Grojsman

Character

A cut grass and lightly fruity fragrance with the background note of flowers smelt at a distance. Demure, very June bride.

Story

Eternity was inspired by the ring, originally a gift from the Duke of Windsor to Mrs Simpson, that Calvin Klein gave to his wife, Kelly Rector, on their wedding day. A simple band of diamonds, it was inscribed with one word: Eternity. So it was for the Windsors, but not for the Kleins, who are now separated. One of many scents playing on the romantic theme of marriage.

Diorissimo

Character

A joy – streamers of lily of the valley fly out on lungfuls of spring air.
First there are the buds and calyx, mingling green sharpness with hints of the flower. This enriches into a heart of lily of the valley with jasmine and lily; the sweetness of the flowers cut with the spicy lemon note of boronia and a little wood. It's almost like the buds opening on your skin.

'For years I studied lily of the valley,' said perfumer Edmond Roudnitska. 'In springtime I gathered huge bouquets in my garden, immersed myself totally in their fragrance, and then all the rest of the year I worked from memory. That's how we were finally able to bring out Diorissimo in 1956. It was the scent of the flower, captured and transposed into a perfume that women could wear.'

From his Eau Fraîche de Dior onwards (1953), there is a clear signature to the scents by this master-perfumer, especially Diorissimo, Eau d'Hermès, Eau Sauvage and Diorella. At this point, he viewed the scents of the day as 'too gourmandise; they were more like bonbons than perfumes'. Instead, he aimed for clarity, which is a hallmark of his work, and the maxim 'faîtes simple'. Perhaps the best ever portrait of a flower.

Top notes	
Lily of the valley buds, bergamot, rosewood	
Middle notes	
Lily of the valley, ylang-ylang, amaryllis, boronia	
Base notes	
Jasmine, sandalwood, civet	

House	Christian Dior
Date	1956
Perfumer	Edmond Roudnitska

Story

The great French couturier Christian Dior was highly superstitious.
He visited clairvoyants; had a lucky number, eight; a lucky letter, M; a lucky colour, red; and his lucky charms: stars and lily of the valley. He adored this flower and hid a sprig in every outfit in his collections. In France, the flower is also given to young girls on the first of May. Diorissimo was launched with a limited edition of a Baccarat crystal bottle stoppered with a bouquet of gilded bronze flowers. Dior died a year later, having appointed the young Saint Laurent his protégé. Diana, Princess of Wales wore this scent.

Lily of the Valley

Top notes
Bergamot
Middle notes
Lily of the valley
Base notes
Sandalwood, oakmoss

House	Penhaligon
Date	1976
Perfumer	unknown

Character

A Victorian-type formula ideal for those who love simple floral fragrances. The crushed leaf and citrus note is in piquant contrast to the honey note of the flower.

Story

In the 1860s a Cornish barber William Henry Penhaligon left his native Penzance on the south-west coast of England and set up a shop in London's fashionable Jermyn Street. The company gained royal warrants, but had begun to languish by the 1970s when it was bought by Sheila Pickles who, armed with Penhaligon's original formulae books, resuscitated it. Since then, the company has been awarded a royal warrant by His Royal Highness the Prince of Wales. The company is now owned by Warnaco.

Après L'Ondée

Top notes
Bergamot, aniseed
Middle notes
Violet, heliotrope, hawthorn
Base notes
Orris, musk, ambrette seeds

House	Guerlain
Date	1906
Perfumer	Jacques Guerlain

Character

Hawthorn and violets are doused in rain and come up cold and shivering. Cold scents of this type are rare. Its austere character comes from the liquorice-like aniseed note allied to the almond aroma of heliotrope. Underneath, way down, lies the echo of warmth in orris and musk-like ambrette seeds: Garbo-esque.

Story

This rare scent is like a secret; Guerlain do not promote it, and few find it. It's not widely available. The name means 'after the shower', and never was a scent more aptly named. At the same time, it has a cerebral quality. For brainy types.

Heliotrope

Top notes	
Bergamot, petitgrain, almond	
Middle notes	
Ylang-ylang, rose, jasmine	
Base notes	
Tonka bean, vanilla, balsam of Peru, musk	

House	Etro
Date	1990
Perfumer	Robertet

Character

Heliotrope flowers have a distinctive almond odour, instantly detectable in this fragrance in which you will also catch the vanilla smell of pastry. The heliotrope plant is also known as Cherry Pie, perhaps because pies were traditionally made with marzipan which has an almond smell. Elegant and unlike anything else around now.

Story

In the Victorian language of flowers, heliotrope stood for 'devotion'. Most fragrances with heliotrope, like this one, are made synthetically. Etro are an Italian company known for their accessories and luggage, especially in paisley pattern.

Blue Grass

Top notes	
Aldehydes, lavender, bergamot, neroli, orange	
Middle notes	
Jasmine, carnation, rose, tuberose, narcissus, clove, pepper, nutmeg	
Base notes	
Sandalwood, vetiver, cedar	

House	Elizabeth Arden
Date	1936
Perfumer	Georges Fuchs

Character

A dew-fresh floral that is not too flowery; rounded with cool, balmy lavender, and underpinned with clean woods and spices. Modern women should rediscover it as a sports fragrance.

Story

Florence Graham established her beauty salon in 1910 on Fifth Avenue, New York. She named it Elizabeth Arden, after the popular book *Elizabeth and her German Garden* and herself adopted this name. It grew to be one of the most successful beauty companies ever. This scent, developed by a perfumer from the old Grasseois house of Fragonard, was named for the Kentucky 'blue grass' in honour of the horses at Arden's stud. 'You'll never sell it with that name', one of her managers famously complained, 'it will remind people of manure.' It became her best-selling fragrance.

Eau d'Eté

Top notes
Lime, grapefruit, sweet orange
Middle notes
Jasmine, rose, cinnamon
Base notes
Musk, balsam

House	de Nicolaï
Date	1997
Perfumer	Patricia de Nicolaï

Character

Fresh head notes with a delicious accent of sweet orange followed by a classic jasmine-rose accord with a touch of cinnamon. More enduring than most eaux de toilettes.

Story

Eau d'Eté comes from a small independent house owned by 'nose' Patricia de Nicolaï, a descendant of the Guerlain family. 'The big manufacturing houses are the best places to train,' says de Nicolaï, 'but after that the work is very limited, you are not free to create fragrances you love. You are like a bridled horse.' Free from constraints, de Nicolaï can use essences such as mimosa or neroli, rarely used because of their cost. Patricia de Nicolaï is now based in London.

L'Ombre dans L'Eau

Top notes
Blackcurrant leaves
Middle notes
Blackcurrant buds, rose de mai
Base notes
Amber, musk

House	Diptyque
Date	1983
Perfumer	Desmond Knox Leet

Character

Diptyque described this perfume as 'the scent of a green riverside garden'. Crystalline rose with green blackcurrant leaves and just a faint tang of the fruit. Celestial purity.

Story

The Diptyque scents are unique. Yves Coueslant and partner Desmond Knox Leet used to stride over Mount Athos, thrusting wild plants into a suitcase which they delivered to Grasse, with the instructions 'bottle this' (for L'Eau Trois). Other scents are inspired by descriptions from the time of Alexander the Great (Eau Lente – 'the smell of bronze' said Knox Leet) or a sixteenth-century pomander (L'Eau). They also created the best ever scent for a tropical heatwave, the virulently green Virgilio.

AnaïsAnaïs

Character

Soft-focus ads, soft-focus smell. The galbanum gives a herbaceous beginning which bleeds into the heart note of jasmine, honeysuckle and rose for a clean, airy feel. The result is tender and innocent, and very light on the base notes.

Story

Since the 1960s, perfume houses have been obsessed with attracting a younger clientele. Charlie, launched in 1973, showed it could be done with phenomenal success. AnaïsAnaïs proved even more phenomenally successful in the long run, but by taking a different approach. Instead of being bold, 'out there' and in trousers, the image of the scent from the beginning was anti-feminist, passive, secretive. It is not a lifestyle fragrance, it's about virginal creatures discovering their sensuality. AnaïsAnaïs is a Lolita perfume, encapsulating all the gushing sentimentality and narcissism of the tender-hearted teen. This triumph of marketing was overseen by the brilliant Annette Louit, who then worked at L'Oréal, which owns Parfums Cacharel.

Cacharel is a French fashion house with a retro style specializing in knitwear. They used photographer Sarah Moon, famous for her grainy shots of flower-like girls, for their advertising. Moon also shot Cacharel's memorable scent ads featuring doe-eyed, dreamy, almost narcotized girls who look as though they'd rather nuzzle each other than any brute male. The design of the bottle was another coup. In white opaline glass with a silver stopper, it was inspired by an antique toiletry set spotted in London.

The name comes from Anaïtis, ancient Persian goddess of love. It makes everyone think of Anaïs Nin, most famous for her erotic tales, *Delta of Venus* – definitely a book on every teen girl's hit list at the time.

Top notes	
Galbanum, hyacinth, bergamot, orange flower, fruit note	
Middle notes	
Jasmine, honeysuckle, tuberose, lily of the valley, rose, carnation, ylang-ylang, orris	
Base notes	
Sandalwood, cedar, vetiver, amber, incense	

House	Cacharel
Date	1978
Perfumer	Paul Léget, Raymond Chaillan, Roger Pellegrino, Robert Gonnon

Ferragamo Pour Femme

Character

A gust of bracing aniseed air and crisp leaves is followed by a distant whiff of fruits and flowers. A drydown of microscopic spice. Fresh, faint and for elegant outdoorsy types.

Story

Salvatore Ferragamo was one of the greatest of all shoe designers. Known as 'the shoemaker to the stars' he hand-made exquisite designs for Hollywood actresses such as Gloria Swanson and later for royalty such as Queen Elizabeth II. He invented stilettoes, cork-soled platforms and wedges. His children have headed the company since his death in 1960. This is the first Ferragamo fragrance. From the side, the sinuous column bottle is meant to look like a footstep.

Top notes
Aniseed, neroli, blackcurrant, buds, green leaves
Middle notes
Orris, rose, peony, nutmeg, pepper, lily of the valley
Base notes
Raspberry, woody note, almond, musk

House	Ferragamo
Date	1998
Perfumer	Jacques Cavalier

First

Top notes
Aldehydes, bergamot, blackcurrant buds, mandarin
Middle notes
Jasmine, hedione, rose de mai, narcissus, orris, ylang-ylang, carnation
Base notes
Vetiver, musk, amber, vanilla, sandalwood

House	Van Cleef & Arpels
Date	1976
Perfumer	Jean-Claude Elléna

Character

Lively and fresh, First is a luminous floral built around the perfumer's love of jasmine. Hedione, derived from the green-floral note found in natural jasmine, enhances the transparency. Hedione was first used in Eau Sauvage, but in First it is used at ten times that strength. A little carnation gives a warm, clove tint. The base is discreet and woody; a tender fragrance.

Story

This was the first of the jeweller perfumes that have since been so successful. These prestigious Parisian jewellers, dating back to 1906, are still in the hands of the Arpels family. The shape of the bottle comes from a gold and diamond pendant they designed, and the cap is the basic pendant, upside down.

Secrete Datura

Character

This intriguing scent has something of the gentle sweetness of linden blossom. It has a fresh air feeling and a smooth, ductile heart note of very soft, but enduring, flowers rounded by orris.

Story

The datura, a plant of the nightshade family, is known as 'the sorcerer's herb'. The powdered seeds or leaves were reputedly used to induce sleep, hallucinations or even death. It releases its odour at night. Jean Laporte found the scent 'bewitching . . . I was seduced by this treacherous plant, and captivated by its extraordinary perfume'. Inspired by the 'master perfumers and glove-makers' of earlier centuries, Jean Laporte opened his boutique in Paris in 1988. He formerly owned L'Artisan Parfumeur.

Top notes
Lemon, heliotrope, lily
Middle notes
Jasmine, honeysuckle, neroli, wallflower
Base notes
Orris, vanilla, sandalwood

House	Maître Parfumeur et Gantier
Date	1991
Perfumer	Jean François Laporte

French Lime Blossom

Top notes
Bergamot, petitgrain, orange flower
Middle notes
Tarragon, lime blossom, jasmine, rose
Base notes
Honey, wood notes

House	Jo Malone
Date	1994
Perfumer	Jo Malone

Character

This reminds me of Paris and, indeed, Jo Malone says she was inspired to create this scent when walking under the linden trees along the Champs Elysées in early summer. Lime or linden blossom (known in French as Tilleul) has a highly individual smell. Soft, limpidly sweet, it has a childlike innocence. A touch of bergamot adds freshness.

Story

Jo Malone is the daughter of London's skincare guru Aileen Malone, a woman as well known for her discretion as her healing hands. Learning the business at her mother's knee, Jo went on to establish her own hugely successful beauty salon, skincare range and fragrance line, now owned by Lauder. Rather chicly, she also designed a fragrance for McDonald's hand wipes.

Noa

Character

A shy little thing composed of only fifteen ingredients. Silvery and mildly fruity with a sweet, but light, floral heart. Fades quickly leaving a milky softness followed by a bitter-sweet coffee and coconut aroma. For nuns and virgins.

Story

Cacharel's 'spiritual' sell for the 1990s is, like many scents that came after L'Eau d'Issey, crystal-clear. The 'pearl' tumbling inside symbolizes a 'fragile life-force', say Cacharel, 'a token of stardust and wisdom'. The bottle is very holdable, like a pet rock.

Top notes	
Blackcurrant leaves	
Middle notes	
Peony	
Base notes	
'White' musk, benzoin, incense, coffee	

House	Cacharel
Date	1998
Perfumer	J. Olivier Cresp

Antonia's Flowers

Top notes	
Freesia, linalool	
Middle notes	
Jasmine, magnolia, lily	
Base notes	
Sandalwood	

House	Antonia Bellanca-Mahoney
Date	1984
Perfumer	Bernard Chant

Character

A simple yet beautiful freesia scent, with a delicate sensuous undertone. It has the silky softness of an aroma-chemical called linalool found abundantly in rosewood. Light daywear.

Story

Antonia Bellanca-Mahoney opened her flower shop in the Hamptons on Long Island in 1981. A few years later: 'I had never worn a fragrance in my life. And decided around the tender age of twenty-six that perhaps I should start. I set about looking for a fragrance . . . but to me everything smelt like old ladies, and I was looking for something subtle and light, something that smelled like my flower shop.' So, working with IFF (International Flavours and Fragrances), she launched her own, the first to use headspace technology. It has become a cult favourite. Not surprisingly – there's nothing else quite like it.

L'Eau d'Issey

Character

Issey Miyake said he wanted a scent that smelt of water. He didn't get it. His fragrance certainly does have the quality of flowers drenched in dew, however. It is transparent, light, flowery and feminine, and slightly mysterious, with intriguing fantasy wood notes in the base – a good daytime scent.

Story

Issey Miyake, the avant-garde Japanese designer, had been under contract to cosmetics company Shiseido for some time to produce a fragrance, when French-woman Chantal Roos was called in to head up their new fragrance division, Beauté Prestige Internationale. 'He wasn't keen,' she recalls. 'He said he hated every smell except water. For him, fragrance was a vulgar, Western thing.'

He was not likely to be a fan of Roos, the woman who helped launch the strongly scented Opium for Yves Saint Laurent. For a while, says Roos, 'we were at it cats and dogs'. But Miyake was lucky. Roos' genius lies in understanding how to distil the essence of a designer's style into fragrance, bottle, name and marketing strategy so it appears like a genuine extension of his fashion philosophy.

Miyake started to communicate with her, sending her books, taking her to museums. But when she sent samples, he would still tell her: 'I don't like it. I only like water'. Eventually Roos joked, 'OK, let's call it l'Eau d'Issey [Issey's water] then'. The name stuck. Roos put together a presentation on the water theme, and Miyake became interested. The perfume went on to become a modern classic and the key influence on the nineties trend for light, aqueous florals. Roos has now been poached back to Yves Saint Laurent.

Top notes	
Cyclamen, rosewater, freesia, freshwater ozonic notes	
Middle notes	
Carnation, peony, white lily	
Base notes	
Ambrette seed, synthetic wood notes, tuberose, osmanthus	

House	Issey Miyake
Date	1992
Perfumer	Jacques Cavalier

Parfum d'été

Character

A limpid, sweet, and typically 1990s fragrance. The fresh, watery note of green sap meant to re-create the smell of a garden at dawn blends with a flower bouquet. Fades into a light, musky base.

Story

Kenzo was a Japanese designer, now retired. In 1970 he opened his Jungle Jap boutique in Paris, making clothes inspired by traditional Japanese shapes, but fresh and modern, often in bright patterns. With Parfum d'été he wanted to create a fragrance that would remind people of summer all year round. The bottle by Serge Mansau, is imprisoned in ghostly layers of leaves with a transparent dewdrop on the top.

Top notes	
Green leaves, sap, peach, rosewood	
Middle notes	
Hyacinth, freesia, narcissus, peony, rose, ,jasmine	
Base notes	
Musk, amber, oakmoss, sandalwood, orris	

House	Kenzo
Date	1992
Perfumer	Christiane Mathieu

Pleasures

Top notes	
Green note, freesia, fruity note, violet leaves	
Middle notes	
Rose, peony, lily of the valley, lilac, lily, jasmine, karo-karounde blossom, baie rose	
Base notes	
Sandalwood, patchouli, cedar, amber, musk	

House	Estée Lauder
Date	1995
Perfumer	panel at Firmenich

Character

Chiffon florals with lots of freesias, rose and peony and a melon-like emollience. Baby-soft.

Story

A massive global success, Pleasures contains two unusual ingredients. Karo-karounde is the blossom of a West African shrub similar to jasmine with a touch of hawthorn. Baie rose, grown in the island of Réunion, has been prized as a spice since the fifth century but never used in perfumery before. Lauder employed a new technique – 'soft extraction' – to produce it. Carbon dioxide in a supercritical state between liquid and gas is passed through the raw material and 'softly' extracts the essence, leaving no imprint on the smell. The result is a purer extract with more of the natural top notes intact.

Contradiction

Character

The adult equivalent of baby powder: an everywoman's fragrance that is sweet and pleasant, but a little boring. Sheer, soft florals with a watery drydown that blends well with the skin.

Story

After the ground-breaking marketing of cK one, Klein played it safe with Contradiction. Safe smell, safe ads, sleek bottle. Where's the contradiction? Well, apparently, it's in the woman who wears it. She is 'strong and confident, but still feminine and sensual . . . inspired by modern life in the new millennium'.

Top notes

Chinese eucalyptus, pepper flower, syringa, to-yo ran orchid

Middle notes

Lily of the valley, jasmine, rose, peony

Base notes

Tonka bean, satinwood, sandalwood

House	Calvin Klein
Date	1998
Perfumer	panel at Givaudan Roure

Ultraviolet

Character

Green to begin with, Ultraviolet's watery transparency remains as pepper and the soft apricoty odour of osmanthus develops. A milky note emphasizes the warmth of your skin.
A wearable version of a popular late 1990's theme.

Top notes

Aqueous notes, capsicum

Middle notes

Osmanthus

Base notes

Amber, vanilla

House	Paco Rabanne
Date	1999
Perfumer	Jacques Cavalier

Story

As the eclipse of August 11, 1999 approached, Paco Rabanne announced that the Mir space station was going to crash into Paris and destroy it, as predicted by Nostradamus. 'Mir in Russian means peace,' he explained in his book *1999: Fire from Heaven*. 'Nostradamus talks a lot about peace and also about "l'onde mur", the wall-like wave. If you invert the "u" in "mur" you get "n", and capital "N" in Russian is pronounced "I". So "mur" equals mnr and MNR equals Mir.' Rabanne also believes he has been around for over 78,000 years in various incarnations. He promised to stop talking like that and stick to fashion if the cataclysm did not occur. Back to frocks then.

So De La Renta

Character

Typical of the 1990's trend for aqueous, fruity florals. The top note is freesia, mango and kiwi with a melony overtone. 'Wet' gardenia is supposed to evoke gardenias drenched in dew, while the pimento leaves in the heart aim for a 'humidor' effect. A fragrance full of fantasy notes: prunella is inspired by plums, the wood note by satinwood from de la Renta's native Dominican Republic. Sampanguita is a Filipino flower similar to jasmine, but stronger, with more indole (animal note).

Story

Based in New York, Oscar de la Renta is a designer whose clothes are popular with 'ladies who lunch'. He now also designs for the French couture house of Balmain.

Top notes
Watermelon, mango, kiwi, clementine, cardamom, freesia, 'wet' gardenia

Middle notes
Pimento, sampanguita, narcissus, tuberose, peony, lotus

Base notes
Musk, prunella, wood note, vanilla

House	Oscar de la Renta
Date	1997
Perfumer	Firmenich

By

Character

The top note teeters between tingling citrus and a melony accent. The heart is aqueous, slightly gingery flowers, with lots of meek pittosporum (see Knowing, p.106). But something happens when this coalesces with the base notes, making this the sexiest of pastel flower fragrances. One for Lolitas.

Story

Launched with a partner scent for men; the women's version is packaged in leopard print, the men's in zebra. Dolce & Gabbana are an Italian design duo well known for their sexy yet romantic clothes.

Top notes
Clementine, bergamot, lily of the valley headspace, cyclamen

Middle notes
Ginger lily headspace, Tiger lily headspace, pittosporum, violet

Base notes
Vanilla, coffee, cedar, sandalwood, musk

House	Dolce & Gabbana
Date	1997
Perfumer	panel at IFF

Cheap and Chic

Character

Fizzy fruits explode from the bottle with all the gusto of an Alka Seltzer. Then suddenly they're gone and those dreamy, underwater flower notes beloved of the 1990s are left to expire more slowly. Yuzu, in the top note, is described in D&G Feminine below.

Story

Perfumes with a sense of whimsy were a big trend in the 1930s, but fragrance is too serious a business nowadays to allow for much in the way of jokes. The result of all the gravitas – if only they knew it – is often much, much funnier. Top marks to Moschino then for daring to do a kitsch bottle, shaped like Popeye's girlfriend, Olive Oyl, and calling it 'Cheap'.

Top notes
Bergamot, yuzu, petitgrain, rosewood
Middle notes
Baghdad Nymphea headspace, peony, cyclamen, aqueous accord, wild rose headspace, violet, jasmine
Base notes
Vanilla headspace, white orchid headspace, orris, sandalwood, vetiver, musk, amber

House	Moschino
Date	1995
Perfumer	panel at IFF

D&G Feminine

Top notes
Yuzu, water lily, cyclamen, pear, ozone
Middle notes
Tuberose, mimosa, wisteria, lily, heliotrope
Base notes
Musk, sandalwood, vanilla, cashmerande

House	Dolce & Gabbana
Date	1999
Perfumer	panel at IFF

Character

Yuzu is a Japanese citrus, something between a lemon and a tangerine. It's this wonderful smell that opens D&G Feminine, in an accord with a watery ozone note and tart green pear. The heart note smells like sweet white flowers in rapidly evaporating ice. Fades to a pale wood note. More distinctive than many out-and-out feminine scents.

Story

The signature scent of Dolce & Gabbana's diffusion range, D&G, is aimed at a young woman, though older women who enjoy tuberose perfumes should try this lighter, fruitier sister-scent. Dolce & Gabbana describe the top note as a blend of zest and 'fluo-transparent floral crystal'. It's an expression they made up for the tinkling, chilly freshness of this smell.

Dazzling Gold & Dazzling Silver

Character

Clearly the offspring of Pleasures (see p. 33), these scents share its melon-scented impression of underwater gardens. Silver has a cool, sharp green note, is lighter on the flowers, and reminiscent of Barney's Route du Thé in its bubble-bath drydown. Gold is warmer: luscious fruits, especially fig, then hazy flowers. Linear. Pretty and wearable day scents.

Story

Launched as a pair, the Dazzlings looked forward in their positioning to the more seductive scents of 1999, while looking back in their scent structure to the aqueous innocence of the mid-1990s. They come as a twosome because, from the 200 submissions Lauder tested, they couldn't choose between these two.

Top notes	
Silver: lily, sunshine flower, green note, lotus	
Gold: passion-flower, fig	
Middle notes	
Silver: orchid, rose, passion-flower	
Gold: golden cattleya orchid, lei flower, lily	
Base notes	
Silver: magnolia, woody note, ginger lily	
Gold: sandalwood, amber, vanilla	

House	Estée Lauder
Date	1998
Perfumer	unknown

Allure

Top notes	
Bergamot, mandarin, peach, lemon, green note	
Middle notes	
Jasmine, rose de mai, orris, freesia	
Base notes	
Vanilla, cedar, benzoin, tonka bean, vetiver, amber	

House	Chanel
Date	1996
Perfumer	Jacques Polge

Character

With this fragrance, Chanel wanted to 'shatter the traditional fragrance structure of top-heart-base notes' and create, instead, a fragrance with six facets that 'shimmer and overlap, with no one note predominating'. The fragrance does swing between tonic fresh notes, a cosy warmth, bubbly fruits, airy flowers, cosy warmth again, and so on. Anyone who remembers Love's Baby Soft will regress when the final accord kicks in.

Story

Allure was nearly called Poet, Seduction and then Paradis, until the outbreak of the Gulf War apparently led Chanel to consider this latter too frivolous. The name was finally inspired by the eponymous book by erstwhile *Vogue* editor, Diana Vreeland. 'An ugly woman can have allure,' says Karl Lagerfeld, Chanel's designer, 'and a beautiful woman can have none.' But it means different things to different nations. Research revealed it means 'sexy' to Americans and 'elegant' to the French. It's all about the mystery of attraction at any rate.

Indiscret

Character

Not the original perfume, but a revamped version with the predictable fruity notes of the 1990s on a fresh floral background.

Story

This scent by the French couturier was a huge success on its original launch. Lelong also introduced a series of perfumes called A, B and C, then N, for the Christian name of his second wife, Princess Nathalie Paley. He also did humorous presentations like Ting-a-Ling, which came with bells attached. The bottle for Indiscret is based on half-drawn, draped curtains, a Surrealist theme. . . . In the 1930s, Indiscret also came in a box with matching metal cases, one for powder, one for cigarettes – considered glamorous at the time.

Top notes	
Mandarin, orchid, orange flower, bergamot, peach blossom, galbanum, neroli	
Middle notes	
Rose geranium, tuberose, jasmine, ylang-ylang, clove bud, basil, violet leaves, orris, cypress	
Base notes	
Oakmoss, vetiver, patchouli, guaïacwood, sandalwood, white musk, amber	

House	Lucien Lelong
Date	1935
	re-launched
	1997
Perfumer	panel at Mane

Jean-Paul Gaultier

Character

Gaultier instructed perfumer Jacques Cavalier to make a fragrance that would remind him of the powder on his grandmother's dressing-table and acetone (nail-polish remover) – a smell he adores. The result, happily, smells nothing like the stuff you swipe over your nails. Instead, it's light, rosy, with a sparkling fruit top note and a sherbety drydown. Sweet; very wearable.

Story

The enfant terrible of French fashion, Jean-Paul Gaultier was never going to launch a humdrum fragrance. Instead, he has a light-hearted pink one, bottled in a torso wearing a metal corset inspired by the ones he made for Madonna. Instead of a box, it comes in a can 'like the ones for cat food in the supermarket', as he puts it.

Top notes	
Cyclamen, freesia, lotus, rosewater, bergamot, lemon, mandarin, plum, peach	
Middle notes	
Carnation, peony, lily, ginger	
Base notes	
Ambrette seed, woody note, musk, osmanthus, cinnamon, tonka bean	

House	Jean-Paul Gaultier
Date	1993
Perfumer	Jacques Cavalier

Eau de Charlotte

Character

Quirky, light and fresh. Like Eau d'Hadrien, with its perfect marriage of Sicilian lemon and cypress, this is a disarmingly simple harmony of a few ingredients that sing together. Lily of the valley gives a joyful, almost skipping overture, but it's the coalescing of mimosa and blackcurrant buds – with a little kick of cocoa – which makes the 'jam'.

Story

A fragrance created for Goutal's daughter, Charlotte, who loves blackcurrant jam. A beautiful, accomplished woman, Goutal was trained as a concert pianist, then discovered by David Bailey as a model, before falling in love with perfumery in 1977. Her passion for perfumery was palpable and she went against the grain of the 1980s to consistently express a side of femininity that the mainstream companies never touched. She died in 1999.

Top notes

Lily of the valley

Middle notes

Mimosa, blackcurrant buds

Base notes

Cocoa

House	Annick Goutal
Date	1982
Perfumer	Annick Goutal

Champs-Elysées

Character

Slightly candied peach and blackcurrant buds dominate the effervescent, fruity top note. An elegant bouquet of spring flowers follows, accented by a touch of mimosa. The wood notes give cool sophistication, balanced by vanilla warmth. Youthful but tasteful.

Story

The main Guerlain boutique is on the Champs-Elysées in Paris and has a wonderful Belle Époque interior, reeking of the potent soup of all the Guerlain perfumes mingled together. Guerlain launched a scent with the same name in 1904, and in 1914 Baccarat made the famous turtle-shaped crystal bottle for it. The Champs-Elysées or Elysian Fields was the Greek paradise, and the Greeks believed that it was reached by crossing the river Styx on the back of a turtle.

Top notes

Peach, blackcurrant buds, mimosa leaves, aniseed

Middle notes

Mimosa, rose, almond blossom, hibiscus seed

Base notes

Almond wood, vanilla, cedar, sandalwood, styrax

House	Guerlain
Date	1996
Perfumer	Jean-Paul Guerlain

Trésor

Character

There is something about the warmth of peaches that ripens to nectar on a woman's skin (see Mitsouko p. 111) and there's something about roses, something innocent and powdery, which smells like happiness (see Paris p. 57). If you want the magic of both together, try Trésor, one of Sophia Grojsman's many compositions on the theme of the rose. It is built around an accord she code-named 'cleavage', and it smells, she says, like a young woman's décolleté. Heliotrope in the mid-notes gives Trésor an edge; vanilla thickens the sweetness of peach and rose; sandalwood adds sensuality. You can imagine a young mother wearing this. Grojsman describes it as a 'hug me' fragrance.

Top notes
Peach, apricot blossom, white rose, lily of the valley
Middle notes
Lilac, heliotrope, orris
Base notes
Sandalwood, vanilla, musk

House	Lancôme
Date	1990
Perfumer	Sophia Grojsman

Story

Trésor will be forever associated with Isabella Rossellini, daughter of Ingrid Bergman, and the face of Lancôme for many years. Like her, it is above all womanly. It was born from a perfume Grojsman made for herself, code number 2933, and grew into Lancôme's first fragrance in twelve years (after Magie Noire see p. 137).

Grojsman, based at IFF in New York, would not normally have been involved in creating a perfume for a French house, but she happened to be passing through IFF's Paris office when they mentioned they were working on a Lancôme brief. Grojsman was intrigued. She had recently noticed Rossellini's picture above a Lancôme counter and thought that there was the kind of woman who would wear 2933. She sprayed some of the fragrance for her French colleagues and the rest is history.

Van Cleef

Character

Strikes a judicious balance between the unusual and the instantly loveable. There's a clear green note to start, mellowed by orange flower and the sherbety pop of strawberry and raspberry. Sharp fruits and the bittersweet almond essence note of heliotrope keep the floral mid-notes edgy and not too sweet. Then it dries down to coconut nuzzle juice. Sensual – like young girl's skin.

Story

Another quiet success from the French jewellers Van Cleef & Arpels (see First p. 29). This one comes in a crystal bottle faceted like a diamond in front and balancing on a cut diamond point behind, designed by Serge Mansau who also designed Montana and Kenzo's Parfum d'été. Says Jacques Arpels: 'To ornaments which last an eternity, we have added the most evanescent of adornments'.

Top notes
Bergamot, neroli, galbanum, strawberry, orange flower
Middle notes
Rose, jasmine, geranium, heliotrope, ylang-ylang
Base notes
Cedar, tonka bean, vanilla, musk, amber

House	Van Cleef & Arpels
Date	1993
Perfumer	Pascal Giraux

High

Top notes
Grapefruit, lime, kumquat, tangerine, peppermint, pineapple
Middle notes
raspberry, jasmine, violet, carnation
Base notes
musk, cedar, sandalwood orris, patchouli, moss

House	Patrick Cox
Date	2000
Perfumer	Alan Astori

Character

Starts as Britney Spears, ends as Marlene Dietrich. Zestful fruits pop out of the mix first; then a peppery raspberry accord wrapping the flowers in the heart – juicy and saucy. The drydown is a tauntingly unavailable, slightly strident blonde, the raspberry accord reverberating through cool woods and musk-tinged powder.

Story

Canadian Patrick Cox is the most successful shoe designer of the last ten years, famous for his Wannabe line of loafers. At one point he had to hire a bouncer to keep hysterical Wannabe-shoppers in control outside his London flagship store. The chunky bottle of High was inspired by a 1960s ashtray designed by Cema Dese. The box, a blur of speedy colours, is meant to express 'intense experience' – maybe a sugar rush? "I want High . . . to be as zingy as Coca-Cola" says Cox.

Normandie

Character
Totally typical of its time; very powdery with soft, balsamic, almost soapy clean notes. A perfume with impeccable manners.

Story
In 1984 the house of Patou relaunched twelve old Patou fragrances under the name Ma Collection. The formulas were reproduced exactly and the bottles closely follow those originally designed by Louis Süe, who also designed the bottle for Joy. All twelve are intriguing facets of their time, none more so than Normandie, named for the transatlantic liner that first sailed from Paris to New York in 1935. No ship was ever more luxurious, with many leading French artists contributing to the decor. All the first-class passengers on the maiden voyage received a limited edition metal model of the ship with a bottle of Normandie slotted into the funnel. This extraordinary bottle was relaunched as a limited edition.

Top notes	
Carnation	
Middle notes	
Jasmine, rose, opopanax, tree moss	
Base notes	
Vanilla, benzoin	

House	Jean Patou
Date	1935
Perfumer	Henri Alméras

Fleurs de Bulgarie

Character
An intoxicating rush of crystalline rose absolutes makes this the closest thing to walking through a field of rose de mai in the south of France at dawn. Powdery base.

Story
Made especially for Queen Victoria, Fleurs de Bulgarie (Bulgarian flowers) is a reference to the damascene rose absolute, extensively grown in Bulgaria. Still a family-owned company (see Neroli Sauvage p. 72), Creed is the choice of royal families. Fleurissimo was commissioned by Prince Rainier for Grace Kelly to wear on her wedding day (Jackie Kennedy also wore it); Prince Charles favours Green Irish Tweed; while the King of Saudi Arabia commissioned Millesime Imperial. All the bottles in the Millesime range have the name Millesime on the front – the name of the perfume appears on the base. Commissions remain exclusive to their patrons for five years.

Top notes	
Damascene rose	
Middle notes	
Rose de mai, Italian rose, jasmine	
Base notes	
Tincture of ambergris, orris	

House	Creed
Date	1845
Perfumer	Henry Creed

24, Faubourg

Character

The idea behind this fragrance is the smell of a silk scarf. And it does smell like the silk-lined insides of a handbag, into which some *bon chic bon genre* woman has spilt expensive, perfumed, face powder.

Story

The Hermès flagship store has been at 24, Rue du Faubourg Saint Honoré, Paris, since 1879. The scent is inspired by the phenomenally successful Hermès silk scarf. It must be the only fragrance in existence that also comes with its own diminutive silk cushion.

Top notes	
Bergamot, orange, leaf note, orange flower	
Middle notes	
Sambac jasmine, ylang-ylang, tiara flowers, orris	
Base notes	
Amber, vanilla, sandalwood, tonquitine, patchouli	

House	Hermès
Date	1995
Perfumer	Bernard Bourgeois

Ombre Rose

Top notes	
Honey, rosewood, peach, aldehydes	
Middle notes	
Heliotrope, geranium, orris, rose, ylang-ylang	
Base notes	
New mown hay, Virginia cedar, vanilla, sandalwood	

House	Jean-Charles Brosseau
Date	1981
Perfumer	Françoise Caron

Character

First you dive into a glorious pie made with honey and peaches, vanilla, and the almondy 'cherry pie' note of heliotrope. Next, you're inhaling flowers and new-mown hay. The base is expensive face powder with a woody drydown.

Story

Jean-Charles Brosseau, a Parisian accessory designer, fell in love with a fragrance sample that had sat on a shelf for years when he visited the manufacturers, Roure. It reminded him of his aunts, dusted with powder on Sundays. The bottle was originally designed in 1920 for a scent called Le Narcisse Bleu. Brosseau had wanted to call it Sofa, which has different connotations in French. Luckily, it was vetoed for Ombre Rose (rose shadow).

Ivoire

Character

An extremely elegant woody-floral bouquet, opening with light top notes of green galbanum and citrus, softened with camomile, and given piquancy by a touch of spice. The heart is a delicately structured spring bouquet of rose, violet and lily of the valley. Cool, mossy and woody base. Clean, fresh, well-balanced.

Story

Ivoire is French for ivory, an apt name for this sophisticated, cool scent. Pierre Balmain was a great French couturier who died in 1982 (see Jolie Madame p.113).

Top notes
Galbanum, marigold, bergamot, lemon, wormwood, camomile, aldehydes, violet
Middle notes
Damascene rose, violet, lily of the valley, orris, carnation, narcissus, neroli, nutmeg
Base notes
Vetiver, cedar, oakmoss, sandalwood, ladanum, frankincense

House	Balmain
Date	1979
Perfumer	panel at Florasynth

White Linen

Top notes
Aldehydes, green note, peach, mandarin
Middle notes
Damescene rose, pimento, jasmine, lily of the valley, lilac, violet
Base notes
Cedar, amber, vetiver, labdanum, sandalwood, honey, benzoin, civet

House	Estée Lauder
Date	1978
Perfumer	unknown

Character

Tingling, acid punch of aldehydes and green notes cedes to cool, balsamic odours and a little peach. The heart note is serene, undefinable flowers wrapped in soothing vetiver and woods. Very wearable.

Story

Inspired by Mrs Lauder's memories of her grandmother's garden. This perfume has been a bestseller for twenty years, and it now comes in a variation, White Linen Breeze, which features an ozonic note.

Paul Smith Women

Character

Bright and upbeat, with a fruity top note crackling with pepper. A moment of almost washday freshness is followed by sweet flowers aerated by green tea. Subtle base of clean, cool woods with the faintest aureole of blackcurrant and musk. Very wearable.

Story

A first scent from the hugely successful British designer. Paul Smith is best known for his boldly coloured menswear, updating classic British tailoring. The womenswear line, launched in 1993, was originally conceived for the many women who snapped up the small sizes of the men's clothes. The fragrance bottle was designed by architect Sophie Hicks, who also designed Smith's flagship store, Westbourne House, in London's Notting Hill.

Top notes	
Bergamot, clementine, blackcurrant, green pear, pepper	
Middle notes	
Freesia, lily of the valley, geranium, green tea	
Base notes	
Cedar, vetiver, patchouli, tonka bean, musk	

House	Paul Smith
Date	2000
Perfumer	Arthur Burnham

'1000'

Top notes	
Chinese osmanthus, centifolia rose, bergamot, tarragon, angelica	
Middle notes	
Jasmine de Grasse, violet, damascene rose, orris	
Base notes	
Sandalwood, patchouli, vetiver, civet	

House	Jean Patou
Date	1972
Perfumer	Jean Kerleo

Character

Suave, creamy top note of rose with Chinese osmanthus which has an apricot smell. Judiciously balanced with crushed leaf and bergamot. The heart note is all woman: jasmine from Grasse with both centifolia and the richer damascene rose. In '1000' clarity and luxury intertwine.

Story

'1000' ('mille' in French) had a commercial banned in some countries. An elegant Parisian woman watches her husband drive off. No sooner is he gone than she is running out in her couture suit. Cut to . . . our heroine flinging open the door of a seedy apartment to reveal a young stud lounging on a bed. They rip off each other's clothes. Cut to . . . many exhausting hours later, she leaves, sees a church and goes in. At the confessional she whispers: 'Father, I have sinned'. 'How many times, my child?' he asks. The answer, of course, is 1000.

Dolce Vita

Character

A basket of fruits but lightly done; these are not the fake-smelling fruits of many 1990s scents. The heart is spicy with a few flowers. Dry, woody base. Sprightly.

Story

The theme of the 1990s, as far as scent was concerned, was happiness, and this is Dior's version. Dolce Vita, of course, means 'good life'. Masterminded by Maurice Roger, who also oversaw Poison and Dune, it has a less distinctive personality than either. The bottle, with its champagne bubles was designed by Serge Mansau.

Top notes
Bergamot, grapefruit, pineapple, cardamom
Middle notes
Magnolia, rose, rosewood, lily, clove, peach, apricot, plum, heliotrope
Base notes
Orris, sandalwood, cedar, cinnamon, patchouli, vanilla, amber, musk, castoreum

House	Christian Dior
Date	1995
Perfumer	Pierre Bourdon

Chamade

Top notes
Galbanum, hyacinth, green note, aldehydes
Middle notes
Blackcurrant buds, hedione, rose, ylang-ylang, clove bud, lilac
Base notes
Vanilla, benzoin, tonka bean, vetiver, sandalwood, tolu balsam, balsam of Peru

House	Guerlain
Date	1969
Perfumer	Jean-Paul Guerlain

Character

Quite shy, delicate and green floral with hedione, which is based on the fresher, greener side of jasmine and blackcurrant buds, tangy but fresh, used for the first time here The base notes are powdery, balsamic and dreamy.

Story

Perfume critic Luca Turin calls this one of the greatest perfumes of all time. The name comes from a story by Françoise Sagan in which 'son coeur bat la chamade' meaning 'her heart beat wildly'. A 'chamade' was the name given to the drumbeat signalling a retreat used during the Napoleonic wars. The bottle is a stylized version of the shell in Botticelli's *The Birth of Venus*, oddly it's meant to symbolize woman's liberation.

Rive Gauche

Character

Ernest Beaux, creator of Chanel No5, famously said that it smelt 'of a snowy landscape'. It doesn't – but Rive Gauche does. The aldehyde accord in the top notes sprays tingling snow crystals at the back of the nose that melt into frosty flowers with a powdery drydown. Enigmatic and Siberian. What KGB agents would have worn to seduce James Bond.

Story

Until the 1960s, designer fashion meant *haute couture* where each outfit is made-to-measure at prohibitive cost. YSL opened his first ready-to-wear boutique in 1966 and called it YSL Rive Gauche ('left bank', a reference to the side of the River Seine in Paris where young bohemians lived). Five years later he launched a scent with the same name to appeal to young women.

Top notes	
Aldehydes, leafy note	
Middle notes	
Jasmine, rose, orris	
Base notes	
Sandalwood, vetiver, tonka bean	

House	Yves Saint Laurent
Date	1971
Perfumer	panel at Givaudon Roure

Calandre

Top notes	
Bergamot, aldehydes, lemon, green note	
Middle notes	
Rose, lily of the valley, geranium, jasmine, ylang-ylang	
Base notes	
Vetiver, oakmoss, cedar, sandalwood, amber, musk	

House	Paco Rabanne
Date	1969
Perfumer	Michel Hy

Character

A sparkly opening, green and lemony, gives way to a translucent floral accord. You have to strain to catch any questionable 'metallic' tang: maybe there's a slightly sour green whiff as it dies, due to rose oxides.

Story

Paco Rabanne is a designer famous for his futuristic 1960s clothes. In 1964 he produced twelve experimental dresses in plastic and metal, sewn with pliers and a blowtorch instead of needles and scissors. The scandalous collection was the first to be shown on black models who, rather than walk primly down a catwalk, danced wildly on a podium. Rabanne continued in this vein with dresses made of aluminium chain-mail, paper and plastic. He wanted his scent to be as avant-garde, and to smell like a hot car, but the first attempt proved too successful – and unwearable. Enter this one, named Calandre, which is French for a car's radiator grille.

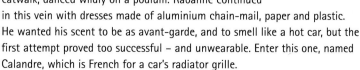

Chanel No5

Character

The smell of the twentieth century. The suaveness of No5 comes from an extravagant proportion of jasmine with rose de mai, orris and neroli blended with vanilla, woody and animal base notes. But the genius is that it doesn't exactly smell like any of them. Chanel said: 'A woman should not smell of roses.' Thanks to the alchemy of aldehyde crystals No5 flies off the skin. Aldehydes have become the hallmark of French perfumery. No5 was the first to use them in quantity. They increase a fragrance's diffusion the way speakers increase the carrying power of your favourite CD. No5 smells luxe; Julie Burchill said it smelt like 'rich mothers'. She also said it smelt 'like a woman in fur'. Yes, and underneath she's wearing lace panties hand-sewn by nuns.

Top notes
Aldehydes, bergamot, lemon
Middle notes
Jasmine, rose de mai, neroli, ylang-ylang
Base notes
Orris, vanilla, sandalwood, cedar, vetiver, musk, amber, civet

House	Chanel
Date	1921
Perfumer	Ernest Beaux

Story

In 1921, Chanel asked a young Russian perfumer, Ernest Beaux, to create a fragrance, the first to carry the name of a couture house (though couturier Poiret had produced scents ten years before). In time, he returned with five samples. Chanel, supine on the sofa with a throbbing headache, told him to leave them on the mantelpiece; she would examine them later. No sooner had Beaux left, however, than she sprang to her feet and sniffed them. When Beaux came back Chanel announced: 'It's number five,' allotting and naming her talisman in one. Five was also Chanel's lucky number. True or myth? We will never know. Though like blind Homer or deaf Beethoven the senses-impairing headache is a mythic sign that this was no ordinary choice – it was psychically inspired.

Another story relates that Beaux's assistant had mistakenly sloshed ten times too much of the aldehydes into the fifth bottle. If so, it was a happy, though unlikely, accident. Edmond Roudnitska, the perfumer and writer, has a more prosaic version. He insists that Beaux had created a perfume for the Russian house Rallet, known as Rallet No1. It had been a flop in Russia. Rallet offered it to Chanel who changed the number to 5. Edmonde Charles-Roux Chanel's biographer, on the other hand, suggests that Beaux first created No5 while working at Coty. Due to its cost Coty hesitated to launch it. Frustrated, Beaux departed with his formula and went to Chanel. What is certain is that in 1927 Coty launched L'Aimant, a perfume almost identical to No5 though never as successful. Later Marilyn Monroe boosted sales of No5 when she claimed to wear nothing else in bed. No5 made Chanel very rich. Ever since, fashion designers have gambled on fragrances to make their fortune.

Arpège

Character

A perfume of potent beauty and refinement. As with Chanel No5, the unctuous floral heart radiates immediately from the skin, thanks to the diffusive power of the aldehydes. Arpège has a classical structure: while the personality of the perfume is harmonious throughout, different elements come to the fore as it develops. At the outset, the rich flower oils are tinged with bergamot. Then the jasmine and rose bloom more forcefully, with the greener note of lily of the valley in the background. The violet accent of orris reverberates for a long time, but there is a moment when the flowers are sunk in warm spicy notes, and another when the cool, dark green tonality of patchouli and vetiver add elegance to the richness. Suave and serene.

Story

André Fraysse, a young perfumer, was hired by couturier Jeanne Lanvin in 1924 to be house perfumer. He created for her what Edmond Roudnitska has called 'the most spectacular tetralogy in the history of perfumery': Arpège (1927), Scandale (1931), Rumeur (1932) and Prétexte (1937). Of the four, only Arpège remains. The word is French for the musical term 'arpeggio' a name given to it by Lanvin's musical daughter, Marie Blanche, Comtesse de Polignac. Jeanne Lanvin was a milliner who began designing clothes for her daughter and friends' daughters. She introduced adults' clothes just before the First World War, often on a mother and daughter theme. By the end of the war, aged 51, she was in charge of a thriving couture business.

Lanvin had perfumes before Arpège, created for her by a Russian of advanced years with the fabulous name of Madame Zed. Her final work for Lanvin was My Sin, a fragrance which saw a phenomenal success in America.

André Fraysse was only in his mid-20s when he began work on Arpège. The scent uses exceptionally high quality flower oils, giving it a rolling richness. The famous spherical black bottle (the 'boule noire') was designed by Art Deco designer Armand-Albert Rateau and engraved with Lanvin's logo, designed by Paul Iribe, which shows Jeanne Lanvin playing with her daughter.

Lanvin remained in family hands until 1996, by which time it had fallen out of favour. Lanvin did not have the budget to compete in a world of multi-nationals. They sold it to L'Oréal, who have nurtured the fragrance, increasing the concentration of perfume oils by 3 per cent in the parfum, and returning it to the high quality it deserves.

Top notes
Aldehydes, bergamot, neroli, peach
Middle notes
Jasmine, damascene rose, ylang-ylang, coriander, clove, orris, tuberose, lily of the valley
Base notes
Vetiver, patchouli, sandalwood, vanilla, styrax, musk

House	Lanvin
Date	1927
Perfumer	André Fraysse

Dali

Character

In Dali's autobiography, he records how he went to woo his wife Gala wearing a stinking brew of fish glue and goat's dung. But then Gala was not your average woman. This commercial scent, licensed in his name, is nothing so bizarre. Instead a fantasy landscape of aldehydes gives way to a rose-jasmine accord accented with lily of the valley.

Story

While working on *Apparition du visage l'Aphrodite de Cnide* in 1981, Salvadore Dali, the Spanish surrealist artist, was approached by the Cofci company to endorse a fragrance. He agreed, and designed the nose and lips bottle. The painting appears on the packaging. Dali died in 1989.

Top notes

Mandarin, bergamot, basil, green note, aldehydes

Middle notes

Rose, jasmine, lily of the valley, tuberose, narcissus

Base notes

Amber, cedar, musk, vanilla, benzoin

House	Salvadore Dali
Date	1985
Perfumer	panel at Cofinluxe

Bois des Iles

Top notes

Bergamot, coriander, petitgrain, aldehydes

Middle notes

Jasmine, rose, orris, ylang-ylang, almond

Base notes

Sandalwood, vetiver, opoponax, musk, tonka bean, vanilla

House	Chanel
Date	1926
Perfumer	Ernest Beaux

Character

Opens in a hardware shop with a smell akin to turpentine. This mellows into an oleaginous stew of exotic flowers, spicy opoponax, vanilla and musk, spiked with sandalwood. Dry, golden base.

Story

'Wood of the Islands' – a perfume redolent of another age, was launched a few years after Chanel No5. Ernest Beaux, who also created Chanel No5, was born in Russia. In his *Souvenirs et Parfums*, Constantin Wériguine notes that when asked for his source of inspiration, Beaux replied: 'Tchaikovsky's *The Queen of Spades* at the Imperial Theatre, Moscow . . . the scenery and the costumes of the period were striking in their richness, and their sumptuousness'.

PARFUM
BOIS DES ILES
CHANEL
PARIS

Madame Rochas

Character

Ineffable French chic. Madame Rochas is a feminine floral with a classic bouquet at the heart and a powdery accent of orris underscored with a little vetiver. The whole is enveloped in the warmth of amber and sandalwood. Delicate.

Story

In 1943 couturier Marcel Rochas fell in love with a beautiful young woman, Hélène, and married her, creating Femme as a wedding gift. In 1955 he died, and his young wife became president of the company with remarkable success, launching this perfume in 1960 when she was thirty. Hélène Rochas was considered one of the chicest women in Paris.

Top notes
Aldehydes, bergamot, lemon, broom, neroli

Middle notes
Jasmine, damascene rose, lilac, lily of the valley, violet, orris, tuberose

Base notes
Amber, sandalwood, cedar, vetiver, musk

House	Rochas
Date	1960
Perfumer	Guy Robert updated by Jean-Louis Sieuzac

L'Interdit

Top notes
Aldehydes, clove, strawberry

Middle notes
Violet, damascene rose, jasmine, jonquil

Base notes
Sandalwood, vetiver, benzoin, amber, patchouli, orris

House	Givenchy
Date	1957
Perfumer	Francis Fabron

Character

Opens with the crystal radiance of aldehydes. The heart is shy violets and roses. One of few available scents with predominant violet. Pearly, a touch of powder.

Story

Couturier Hubert de Givenchy dressed Audrey Hepburn all her life and was a close friend. L'Interdit ('the forbidden one') was created for her and was hers alone for a year, before being launched in 1958 simultaneously with Le De Givenchy. This was the first time a fashion house had launched two perfumes together. In *Breakfast at Tiffany's* (in which she wore Givenchy's clothes), there's a scene where Hepburn sprays herself with scent before going off to visit Uncle Sally in 'Sing-Sing'. It's L'Interdit.

Je Reviens

Character

Built around the noble scent of *Narcissus poeticus*. French *Vogue* editor Joan Juliet Buck was for years addicted to wearing a narcissus absolute: 'It was so concentrated that just a drop on each wrist and two in the bath were enough to send silver running down the walls,' she wrote. 'It set the world throbbing out of control when I wore it. I became a little weird. It was only years later that I read [that] . . . inhaling too much of it can make you go mad.'

Story

Five Worth perfumes link together to tell a story: Dans la Nuit (1924), Vers le Jour (1925), Sans Adieu (1929), Je Reviens (1932), Vers Toi (1934). 'In the night . . . towards dawn . . . without saying goodbye . . . I return . . . towards you'. They really knew how to do romance in those days. There is another story about Je Reviens. Worth say the name came from a famous letter Napoleon sent to Josephine from his campaigning in Italy: 'Je reviens en trois jours . . . ne te laves pas.' ('I return in three days . . . don't wash yourself.') They really knew how to do sex in those days.

Je Reviens became world-famous during the Second World War; it was the scent GIs gave to their sweethearts on leaving Europe, 'je reviens' being interpreted as 'I will return'. The original Charles Frederick Worth, an Englishman, is credited as the man who established the couture when he opened the house of Worth in Paris in 1858. Soon he was court couturier to the Empress Eugénie and dressing the entire haute monde. On his death in 1895, his sons took over, and then his grandsons, Jean Charles and Jacques in 1910. It was under Jean Charles that Parfums Worth was born with Maurice Blanchet as perfumer. Worth worked with René Lalique, the great flacon designer. Dans la Nuit came in a famous Klein-blue ball encrusted with stars. The original bottle for Je Reviens was modelled on a skyscraper, in fluted blue glass. Its best-known incarnation, though, was a simple flat, round bottle in cobalt-blue.

Top notes	
Aldehydes, orange flower, jasmine, ylang-ylang	
Middle notes	
Narcissus, jonquil, clove, hyacinth, orris	
Base notes	
Violet, vetiver, sandalwood, musk, tonka bean, moss	

House	Worth
Date	1932
Perfumer	Maurice Blanchet

Quelques Fleurs L'Original

Top notes
Bergamot, lemon, orange
flower, tarragon
Middle notes
Rose, jasmine, ylang-
ylang, carnation, lily of
the valley, tuberose,
orchid, heliotrope, orris
Base notes
Sandalwood, oakmoss,
amber, tonka bean, musk

House	Houbigant
Date	1912/reworked
	1987
Perfumer	Robert
	Bienaimé

Character

Narcotic orange flower sharpened with green rose and jasmine sing through as the other flowers burst into life. Sweet but fresh, then deepens into an ambery base accord that's very 1980s. Powdery flowers for the final kiss-off.

Story

Quelques Fleurs ('some flowers') is claimed as the first true floral bouquet. Among surviving perfumers, only Floris is older than Houbigant, founded in Paris in 1775.

Everyone from Marie-Antoinette to Tolstoy has indulged in Houbigant – perhaps more than they ought. As Houbigant put it: 'In the spring of 1815, Napoleon was only in Paris for three months – a period that is called The Hundred Days. In those brief months he raised an army and yet found time to shop at Houbigant.' Perhaps if he had concentrated more on his army and less on his aftershave, he might have not lost the ensuing Battle of Waterloo.

Mimosa pour moi

Top notes
Violet leaves,
blackcurrant buds
Middle notes
Mimosa, acacia, jasmine,
lilac
Base notes
Heliotrope, cedar, vanilla,
musk

House	L'Artisan
	Parfumeur
Date	1992
Perfumer	Anne Flipo

Character

The only perfume I know that faithfully captures the milky-musky smell of the winter mimosa. It's a smell unlike anything else, evocative of cats' paws dipped in milk and honey. Spring-like and quite powdery in the base.

Story

The smell of the south of France in spring, though mimosa is not native to France but to Australia and parts of Africa. The trees, with their pale yellow pompoms, start to bloom in February. Branches in bud are cut and forced in mimoseries – barns with long troughs of steaming spring water, onto which the mimosa is thrown to encourage it to open. The open blossoms are then sold in the flower market at Nice.

L'Air du Temps

Character

Virginity, bottled. L'Air du Temps opens with the luminous vapour flowers must exhale on mountain tops. The bergamot and rosewood bring clarity without being brashly citrusy or woody. Then, as the heart note develops, that odour of sanctity is undermined: carnation emerges with its peppery warmth, and peach blending into the skin. The base is powdery orris, cool woods and resins challenged by a faint radiant heat of amber and musk. Airy throughout.

Story

One of the most enduringly popular perfumes, a bottle is sold every five seconds somewhere in the world. Nina Ricci launched her couture house in 1932 with her son Robert Ricci as manager. Robert had a passion for scent.

'Robert Ricci wanted to launch a new fragrance with a floral note', remembers Francis Fabron, the perfumer. 'L'Air du Temps appeals because it is a very simple and explicit bouquet. With no more than 30 ingredients that do not clash with one another, the nose could almost isolate each flower in the composition.' Fabron used a new product – salicylate of benzyl in a massive dose to boost the diffusion of the scent and give a 'linear evaporation'.

The first flacon was a sun with a dove perched on the stopper. Then in 1951 Marc Lalique created the famous stopper with the pair of billing doves. The message of the doves was originally 'peace and love' after the Second World War. But they have come to stand for purity and virginity. Throughout the decades, the print-ads have shown doves nuzzling young girls, girls feeding doves, girls becoming doves.

When Clarisse Starling meets Hannibal Lecter in *The Silence of the Lambs*, he sniffs the air and announces, 'You use Evian skin products, and sometimes L'Air du Temps . . . but not today'. The name means 'spirit of the times'.

Top notes
Bergamot, Sicilian lemon, rosewood
Middle notes
Peach, gardenia, jasmine de Grasse, rose de mai, carnation, ylang-ylang, orchid, pepper, lily
Base notes
Sandalwood, musk, orris, benzoin, cedar, amber, vanilla

House	Nina Ricci
Date	1948
Perfumer	Francis Fabron

Tiare

Top notes	
Tiara, gardenia	
Middle notes	
Tuberose, mimosa, ylang-ylang	
Base notes	
Rosewood, vanilla	

House	Beauté de Chantecaille
Date	1998
Perfumer	Frank Voekl

Character

Typical of the late 1990's trend for light 'living flower' scents. According to de Chantecaille, 'It's delicate, sweet, energizing. It's not a cloying smell, like gardenias from a hothouse. It's alive with the breeze'.

Story

Sylvie de Chantecaille was the creative force behind Prescriptives for nearly 20 years, and helped to develop Calyx. Now she has her own scents, each one aiming to capture an exotic flower from her travels, 'recreating not only the flower,' she explains, 'but the unique experience when, standing beneath a tree, you smell, not just the flower, but the leaf, the night, the wind'. The tiara is a gardenia native to Tahiti. It grows only on coral, forming small bushes covered with white flowers. In Tahiti men wear a closed bud of tiara behind their ears, while women wear an open bloom. Tiara garlands are offered to guests as a sign of welcome.

Attar

Top notes	
Lemon, ylang-ylang	
Middle notes	
Jasmine, carnation	
Base notes	
Incense, musk, vetiver, sandalwood, patchouli, amber	

House	Robert Isabell
Date	1996
Perfumer	Roman Kaiser

Character

A truly modern scent which uses high technology to stay close to nature. This is the most sensual of Isabell's fleeting fragrances. Easy to wear.

Story

Robert Isabell, a New York florist and grand party organizer (think parties for Giorgio Armani, Madonna, Whitney Houston, Ralph Lauren), wanted a collection of fragrances that captured the smell of flowers while they are growing, a type often referred to as 'living flower' scents. He worked with Roman Kaiser at Givaudan Roure to perfect this over five years. It was Kaiser who suggested they also extend the technology to include the odour of smouldering incense for this scent.

Joy

Character

When you have the noblest ingredients, the skill lies in keeping it simple. Jasmine de Grasse, i.e. from Grasse in south-east France, is, by itself, one of the finest odours. Joy's creator, Alméras, added the velvety richness of the damascene rose and the lighter, more lemony rose de mai (May rose). Patou point out that it takes over ten thousand jasmine blooms and 28 dozen roses to make one ounce of Joy. The other ingredients are there to set off this symphony. Sumptuous, yet diaphanous due to the lack of base notes.

Story

Joy is second in worldwide fame only to Chanel No5. According to legend, the successful French couturier Jean Patou set off with his new publicity agent, Elsa Maxwell, the doyenne of café society, to visit Alméras at his laboratory with a view to finding a new fragrance. Alméras offered them phial after phial but nothing pleased them. Finally, in frustration, he said that he had one last offering, a blend of jasmine de Grasse and rose at huge concentrations. As he passed it to Patou he added: 'There's no point considering this one. It's too expensive to market.' Perhaps he knew the effect this would have on two lovers of luxury. Patou and Maxwell swooped on the bottle, cried 'Eureka!' in unison and Joy was born.

It was made available to Patou's couture clients in 1926, and launched on the general market in 1930, perhaps to combat the drastic drop in couture clients due to the Wall Street Crash of 1929. It was Maxwell who penned the immortal ad-line: 'The costliest perfume in the world'.

Top notes
Damascene rose, ylang-ylang, tuberose
Middle notes
Jasmine, rose de mai, honeysuckle
Base notes
There are none

House	Jean Patou
Date	1930
Perfumer	Henri Alméras

J'adore

Character

From the 'dew-drenched flowers' stream of late 1990s perfumes, the most famous of which is Lauder's Pleasures. J'adore smells more European though, like a reworking of the violet and rose handkerchief scents of Victorian times. Green to start, it settles to a sweet but light bouquet. The rather synthetic notes of plum and 'blackberry musk' add a sticky fruitiness to the base.

Story

Champac, dense and sweet, is a popular perfume oil in India. In Oscar Wilde's *The Portrait of Dorian Gray* while musk 'troubled the brain' and violets 'woke the memory of dead romances'; champac was the scent that 'stirred the imagination'. J'adore ('I adore') is Dior's young fragrance. The amphora shape echoes Dior bottles from the 1950s while the gold neck rings refer to the African theme of the spring/summer 1997 Dior prêt-a-porter show.

Top notes	
Champac, mandarin, ivy	
Middle notes	
Orchid, violet, rose	
Base notes	
Plum, amaranth wood, 'blackberry musk'	

House	Christian Dior
Date	1999
Perfumer	Calice Becker

Paris

Character

A rose scent can be insipid, but not Paris. It has the plush texture of dusky cabbage roses, cut with a little alcoholic fruitiness. Sweet, dense. More powdery in eau de toilette.

Story

I wore Paris once on a trip to Paris. Men told me repeatedly I smelt glorious. Maybe it's just the French but Sophia Grojsman, who created it, also told me: 'When I was working on Paris, I wore it home one night and was followed by a drunk. I started to walk quicker and he called out, "Hey lady, I'm not following you. I'm just trying to smell your perfume". I knew then that I had it.' The exquisite bottle, designed to reflect Paris as the City of Light, is by Alain de Mourgues.

Top notes	
Hawthorn, bergamot, juniper berries, carnation, honey, mimosa, orris	
Middle notes	
French, Moroccan and English roses, red fruits, pear liquor, violet	
Base notes	
Musk, amber, cedar, sandalwood, heliotrope	

House	Yves Saint Laurent
Date	1983
Perfumer	Sophia Grojsman

Fleur de Rocaille Classique

Character

Springs from the bottle like a meadow in flower. First, bergamot plays sharply against orange flower, soon complicated with a little warmth of peach. The heart is a tumble of fresh, lively flowers, particularly jasmine, violet and rose. Light base. Simple. More than enough.

Story

Caron are a small French perfume house well worth seeking out. Ernest Daltroff, who owned the company until his death in 1940, was not trained as a perfumer but created many masterpieces, often in collaboration with Michael Morsetti. He bought a small perfume shop on rue Rossini in Paris to acquire the name of Caron, and started with Chantecler in 1906. Karl Lagerfeld has called Fleur de Rocaille 'the best perfume in the world'.

Top notes	
Rosewood, bergamot, orange flower, green note, coriander, peach	
Middle notes	
Jasmine, tuberose, rose, carnation, orris, violet, lilac, mimosa, lily of the valley	
Base notes	
Sandalwood, musk, cedar	

House	Caron
Date	1933
Perfumer	Ernest Daltroff

Giorgio

Top notes	
Green note, bergamot, fruit note, orange flower, aldehydes	
Middle notes	
Tuberose, gardenia, ylang-ylang, orchid, jasmine, rose	
Base notes	
Sandalwood, cedar, moss, musk, amber, camomile, patchouli, vanilla	

House	Giorgio of Beverly Hills
Date	1981
Perfumer	panel at Florasynth

Character

A big, swashbuckling superfloral, Giorgio acted like olfactory shoulderpads for 1980s executive women and started a trend for power-perfumes. It's thick with tuberose and gardenia balanced by a powdery, almost prickly dryness that becomes prevalent as it dries down. Synonymous with brash, bad taste – a pity, because it melds with some women to terrific effect.

Story

The first fragrance to be sold via scent strips in magazines. When it launched, French perfume dominated the market, and it was hard enough to create a world-beater from New York, never mind Beverly Hills. But Giorgio, named for the designer store owned by Gayle and Fred Hayman, was an unstoppable force. The Haymans rolled it out slowly, building a frenzy of desire, and it made them multi-millionaires. Sadly, though, it ended with their acrimonious divorce and suit and countersuit for control of the perfume. It is now owned by Procter & Gamble.

Fracas

Character

The definitive tuberose perfume, which has inspired all others, including Chloë, Gianfranco Ferre and Versace's Blonde. Fracas differs from its successors however. Purer, more concentrated, it projects itself at a needle-sharp pitch. It has a fresh, green nuance due to bergamot and sap which prevents it becoming too dense and heavy. And, from early on, a shadowy musky stink: id to tuberose's radiant ego. But tuberose predominates, a magnificent smell like orange flowers dipped in clotted cream.

Top notes
Bergamot, orange flower, peach, leafy green note
Middle notes
Tuberose, jasmine, orris, rose, carnation
Base notes
Sandalwood, benzoin, oakmoss, musk, cedar

House	Robert Piguet
Date	1948
Perfumer	Germaine Cellier

Story

'She, the tuberose. She would set off on the sirocco wind, cross the road, force open my door with all her flowery might and softly climb the stairs . . . a cloud of dreams bursts forth and grows from a single, blossoming stem, an unthreatened peace.' (Colette) The tuberose has always been the symbol of voluptuousness. Young girls were once forbidden to smell them in case they fell into an intoxicated trance with dire results for their chastity.

Piguet was a Swiss-born Parisian designer of the 1930s and 1940s. Hélène Rochas remembers him as 'always in black, a Protestant look, but a biting humour'. His first scent was Bandit, another classic. Then came Fracas. As French *Vogue* noted in 1997: 'This white flower is a torrid poison which acts seductively on men. It is an agony, an olfactory rape.' And the author went on to lament the disappearance of Fracas from France.

In fact, Fracas was resurrected only a few years ago when Geoffrey Webster, American president of fragrance manufacturing house Givaudan Roure, took out an ad: 'If you are a lover of Robert Piguet's Fracas, the greatest French perfume, call: 1-888 4 FRACAS.' He was inundated by calls. Fracas (the name means 'violent noise') is **the** choice perfume of American society doyennes.

Like Bandit, it was created by one of the greatest perfumers of the century, and a woman: Germaine Cellier. Beautiful, blonde, with green eyes and freckles, she was friends with Cocteau, and sat for André Derain. Her approach was free-spirited and untrammelled by convention. She would arrive for work at ten o'clock and leave at eleven, considering her work done. Cellier dedicated Fracas to a great beauty, Edwige Feuillère.

Envy

Top notes	
Green notes, magnolia	
Middle notes	
Vine-flowers, lily of the valley, jasmine	
Base notes	
Orris, wood notes, musk	

House	Gucci
Date	1997
Perfumer	Maurice Roucel

Character

The ping of a green top note then white flowers wrapped in plastic.

Story

Tom Ford, the American designer who rejuvenated Gucci with his sexy, streamlined designs, has this to say: 'People often feel a little guilty about some of the thoughts they may have about sex, and that's one of the things that makes sex exciting. And it's the same thing about envy. Envy is something everyone feels, whether you want to admit it or not.'

Chloë

Top notes	
Green note, honeysuckle, orange flower, coconut, peach, bergamot, aldehydes	
Middle notes	
Tuberose, jasmine, narcissus, orris, ylang-ylang, hyacinth, carnation	
Base notes	
Musk, sandalwood, amber, moss, benzoin	

House	Chloë
Date	1975
Perfumer	Betty Busse

Character

A vivacious, sweet floral with a warm, almost tropical ambience. The predominant mid-note is tuberose balanced with dry, powdery moss and orris. This is a perfume for women who wear lingerie tinted *cuisse de nymphe émue*.

Story

In the mid-1970s this perfume was a cult. The award-winning bottle, with a stopper meant to represent a calla lily, was designed by Joe Messina with Karl Lagerfeld. As a teenager I thought it represented aorta sprouting from a heart – sort of romantic and Damien Hirst-like at the same time. When the perfume was launched, Karl Lagerfeld was designing floaty chiffons for the label before moving on to Chanel.

Gianfranco Ferre

Character

Classic and well-composed tuberose scent that opens against a green background with a little bergamot. The tuberose heart unfolds slowly, rich but remaining buoyant and airy. Unlike some tuberose perfumes, it's not strident nor over-poweringly sweet. Rather *grande dame*.

Story

The first scent from the Italian designer, who went on to design for Dior before he left to make way for John Galliano.

He now designs his own collection from Milan. He started out designing for a furniture company and his clothes retain an intellectual, architectural quality with strong blocking of colours.

Top notes
Fruit note, green note, bergamot, orange flower, coriander, hyacinth
Middle notes
Tuberose, jasmine, lily of the valley, rose, orris, narcissus, orchid, honeysuckle
Base notes
Cedar, sandalwood, benzoin, civet, musk, amber

House	Gianfranco Ferre
Date	1984
Perfumer	unknown

Beautiful

Top notes
Bergamot, lemon, cassis, thyme, clary sage
Middle notes
Tuberose, jasmine, carnation, orange flower, lily of the valley, ylang-ylang
Base notes
Vetiver, sandalwood, musk, cedar, vanilla

House	Estée Lauder
Date	1986
Perfumer	unknown

Character

Green and citrus top note flees before a big bridal bouquet groaning with tuberose and orange flower. Extravagant, creamy, romantic and sweet. Ideal on a country and western singer.

Story

The story goes that Mrs Lauder worked for four years on this fragrance – with which perfumer, we are not told – before she felt ready to try it on some friends. Armed with a small laboratory atomizer, she set off for lunch. The friends were duly sprayed. 'Ooh,' they kept saying, 'it's – beautiful'. Hence the name. Lauder's bridal fragrance, always advertised with a model in full wedding regalia.

Fragile

Character

Razor-sharp, intensely sweet and dominated by tuberose – a familiar and very feminine odour. A touch of the late 90s caramel pie in the base. Surprisingly womanly given the bottle.

Story

Adorable object, inspired by the snow domes Gaultier loved as a child. As the millennium ended, women regressed to the mental age of My Little Pony. Cosmetics turned glittery and perfumes became toys that smelt of sweets or milk. No designer understands your inner child like Gaultier, and Fragile is the epitome of this trend. The liquid inside the dome is the perfume; a grid inside catches the gold flakes when you spray the scent. Comes packaged in plain cardboard with 'fragile' stamped all over like shipping instructions.

Top notes	
Orange, raspberry leaves	
Middle notes	
Tuberose, capsicum,	
pink pepper	
Base notes	
Cedar, violet wood, musk	

House	Jean-Paul Gaultier
Date	1999
Perfumer	Jacques Cavalier

Carolina Herrera

Top notes	
Orange flower, bergamot, apricot, aldehydes	
Middle notes	
Tuberose, hyacinth, jasmine, honeysuckle, narcissus, ylang-ylang	
Base notes	
Sandalwood, cedar, moss, vetiver, civet	

House	Carolina Herrera
Date	1988
Perfumer	panel at Firmenich

Character

Operatic white flowers, chiefly jasmine and tuberose. Forward, sweet and ultra-feminine.

Story

A socialite prominent on the best-dressed list, Herrera started her own fashion house in 1981 at the late age of 42. Until launching this scent she mixed her own from tuberose and jasmine oils, an undiluted fix of heady florals which is rumoured to have enslaved New York's taxi drivers. 'This fragrance has very personal associations for me,' she says. 'I had a very happy childhood in Venezuela and there was a beautiful vine of jasmine under my bedroom window. I think, subconsciously, I associate jasmine with happiness.' As for tuberoses, her mother used to fill the house with them.

Carolina Herrera
eau de toilette
natural spray

Blonde

Top notes	
Bergamot, neroli, gardenia, orange flower	
Middle notes	
Tuberose, jasmine, narcissus, violet leaves, broom, everlasting flower, orris	
Base notes	
Sandalwood, musk, civet, amber, moss	

House	Versace
Date	1995
Perfumer	panel at Givaudan Roure

Character

'Take no prisoners' tuberose typhoon. The opening is sharp yet heavy, almost like some new hallucinogenic glue. But according to Versace, the cyborg rampaging up your nostrils is not synthetic, it's nature red in tooth and claw. When this dies, tuberose thumps in, boosted by a phalanx of powerful floral cohorts. An ox-feller.

Story

The Medusa head, which is Versace's logo, is appropriate on the bottle here. She would have been big enough to wear Blonde. The scent was created in tribute to and with the input of Donatella Versace, designer Gianni's younger sister and muse. She appears, photographed by Richard Avedon, in the print-ads. Donatella has designed the Versace collections since her brother's death in 1997.

White Diamonds

Top notes	
Amazon lily, neroli, aldehydes	
Middle notes	
Tuberose, jasmine, ylang-ylang	
Base notes	
Amber, patchouli, oakmoss, civet, musk, sandalwood	

House	Elizabeth Taylor
Date	1991
Perfumer	Carlos Banaim

Character

An intense rush of white flowers. For women who are not afraid of scatter cushions.

Story

An appropriate title for a scent launched under Elizabeth Taylor's name. After all, in an age when most women are more interested in mantras, she remains as a symbol of passionate love expressed through the time-honoured tribute of whopping great rocks. Her most famous husband, Richard Burton, wrote of their first meeting: 'She took off her sunglasses and looked at me . . . aeons passed, civilizations came and went, brave men and cowards died in battles not yet fought, while those cosmic headlights examined my flawed personality.' Afterwards he gave her the 33.19 karat Krupp diamond.

Lalique

Character

One of those scents of such high-pitched sweetness you feel it could shatter crystal. Perhaps appropriately, considering Marie-Claude Lalique envisaged it as 'un parfum de cristal'. Basically, it's the scent of hothouse flowers with lots of blackberry intensifying the effect.

Story

René Lalique is regarded as the greatest scent bottle designer. His closest partnership, beginning in 1906, was with François Coty. His son, Marc, designed one of the best-loved flacons of all time, for L'Air du Temps, and his grand-daughter, Marie-Claude Lalique, runs the Lalique crystal business today, and designs the bottles for this scent. A new limited edition flacon for the parfum is issued each year.

Top notes

Gardenia, blackberry, mandarin, orange flower

Middle notes

Jasmine, tuberose, orange, magnolia, damascene rose, ylang-ylang

Base notes

Sandalwood, cedar, vanilla, musk, amber

House	Lalique
Date	1992
Perfumer	Max Gavary

Amarige

Character

High-pitched and hot-tempered. Cassis blusters from the bottle first, then exotic flowers and spicy fruits follow pell-mell.

Story

The name is an anagram of the French *mariage* (marriage). Amarige was created as 'the embodiment of happiness'. It is certainly vibrant and powerfully fruity – notes which, psychologists tell us, are associated with happiness.

Top notes

Plum, tangerine, orange flower, violet, rosewood

Middle notes

Cassis, gardenia, ylang-ylang, jasmine, tuberose, orchid, acacia farnesiana, 'dried red fruits'

Base notes

Amber, musk, tonka bean, vanilla, sandalwood, cedar, cashmerande

House	Givenchy
Date	1991
Perfumer	Dominique Ropion

Bijan Light

Top notes	
Ylang-ylang, narcissus, orange flower	
Middle notes	
Jasmine, lily of the valley, damascene rose	
Base notes	
Patchouli, oakmoss, sandalwood	

House	Bijan
Date	1995
Perfumer	panel at Givaudan Roure

Character

This is the lighter, hence the thinking went, more 1990s version of Bijan's signature scent. Let that give you some idea of how strong the original is. What comes to mind: torrid flowers in an electric storm. A mad scientist's laboratory has exploded in the vicinity.

Story

Bijan Pakzad, the ebullient Persian menswear designer, opened his first store in Beverly Hills in 1976. His approach seemed to sum up the 1980s love of élitism and luxury at all costs. He also has a fragrance called DNA in a double helix bottle, named for the initials of his three children, although of course it also means dioxyribonucleic acid, the stuff of your genes.

L'Heure Bleue

Top notes	
Aniseed, bergamot, neroli, coriander, clary sage	
Middle notes	
Clove bud, damascene rose, jasmine, heliotrope	
Base notes	
Vanilla, orris, musk, benzoin	

House	Guerlain
Date	1912
Perfumer	Jacques Guerlain

Character

The bittersweet smell of aniseed, then clove and almond-like heliotrope in the mid-notes give L'Heure Bleue a distinctive character. The heart is heady flowers swaddled in the velvety Guerlain base notes with a powdery touch.

Story

Jacques Guerlain intended this perfume to be a tribute to the Impressionists whom he collected. The name means 'blue hour' in French, the hour of dusk when the odour of flowers intensifies. Joan Juliet Buck of French *Vogue* wore L'Heure Bleue and was told by a famous old screen writer that she looked like Hedy Lamarr. In fact, as she explained: 'I smelled the way Hedy Lamarr looked.'

Sublime

Character

One of those fragrances that instantly affect the mood. The orange and mandarin in the top note smell happy and sunny, allied to the freshness of bergamot and green notes with the huskiness of some spice. The central flower accord is well-balanced; never too sweet.

Story

It's not as famous, perhaps, as Joy, but this scent from Patou is joyful and uplifting. The bottle is meant to hint at a ripe fruit; the stopper is a spring bud bursting. The yellow sunrays on the box well express the zest of the scent.

Top notes	
Orange, mandarin, coriander, green note	
Middle notes	
Rose, jasmine, lily of the valley, orange flower, ylang-ylang, carnation	
Base notes	
Vanilla, vetiver, sandalwood, oakmoss	

House	Jean Patou
Date	1992
Perfumer	Jean Kerleo

Escada

Top notes	
Bergamot, hyacinth, osmanthus, mandarin	
Middle notes	
Tuberose, orange flower, ylang-ylang, jasmine, carnation	
Base notes	
Sandalwood, vanilla, orris, frankincense, myrrh, cedar	

House	Escada
Date	1990
Perfumer	Michel Almairac

Character

For the ultra-feminine luxury-lover. Escada is a heavy-lidded floral bouquet dominated by tuberose and jasmine, the most carnal of flowers. The bergamot and mandarin top notes make a hurried appearance before this lush heart sprawls. Ylang-ylang follows. Spicy and vanilla-accented base.

Story

Escada is a German-based fashion house launched by the Swedish designer Margaretha Ley. The clothes are often tailored, conservative but in bold colours. Every summer, Escada also launch a scent to complement their spring/summer collection.

5th Avenue

Character

A rich, ladylike floral with the modern twist of delicately played fruity top notes. The base notes are warm, enveloping and semi-oriental.

Story

The design of the parfum bottle is inspired by the Manhattan skyline. The message is a kind of Charlie for the 90s – 5th Avenue is aimed at an independent, spirited woman with work to do. The famous New York street is also the location of the most famous of the Elizabeth Arden salons.

Top notes

Lilac, linden blossom, lily of the valley, mandarin, bergamot, pineapple, apple, peach

Middle notes

Freesia, damascene rose, violet, ylang-ylang, jasmine, tuberose, clove, nutmeg

Base notes

Amber, musk, sandalwood, orris, vanilla

House	Elizabeth Arden
Date	1996
Perfumer	Jimmy Bell

Birmane

Top notes

Kumquat, peach, freesia

Middle notes

Lily, jasmine, rose

Base notes

Tonka bean, musk, cedar

House	Van Cleef & Arpels
Date	1999
Perfumer	Richard Herpin

Character

Tart, fizzy fruit opener, with detectable kumquat – an original fruit note. Soon warms into a more musky, chocolaty warmth sweetened with flowers.

Story

All of Van Cleef's scents are 'associated' with a gem – appropriately, as they are jewellers. The finest rubies come from Burma, from a valley called Mogok said to be guarded by tigers and eagles. Jewellers call their best quality rubies the 'Burmese'. Hence the name of this scent, French for 'Burmese'. The bottle is a glass version of the step-cut used for the hardest stones. The round stopper is meant to echo a cabochon ruby.

The
fruity
Family

Chapter 2

The use of citrus fruits such as lemon,
bergamot and orange, dates back to the
eaux de Colognes of the 17th century.
They are widely used in perfumery for their
sparkle and freshness (see also the citrus
sub-section of the Herbaceous Family).
In the 1990s, there was a massive trend
for a wider range of fruit notes especially
more exotic fruits like fig, plum, raspberry,
mango and blackcurrant or cassis, as well
as the aroma of steamed fruit puddings.
Fruity fragrances continue to have a wide
appeal due to their typically youthful,
upbeat quality.

Eau d'Hadrien

Top notes
Sicilian lemon, grapefruit, bergamot, galbanum
Middle notes
juniper berry, basil
Base notes
Citron wood, cypress, light musk

House	Annick Goutal
Date	1981
Perfumer	Annick Goutal

Character

While many modern fruit scents smell like saccharine plastic imitations, this, if anything, smells more brilliantly alive than the real thing. Sicilian lemons come tumbling out of the bottle golden and razor-sharp, eventually rounded by a little grapefruit. Underscored by the smoky, slightly sultry aroma of cypress wood.

Story

A modern cult classic, beloved by everyone from Madonna to Mitterand. Eau d'Hadrien's slow climb ushered in the clean, fresh revolution of the 1990s. It's named for the Roman emperor – he of the Wall – as described in *Memoirs of Hadrian* by Marguerite Yourcenar. Reading it, Goutal imagined the emperor – a refined intellectual – wearing this.

Citrus Paradisi

Top notes
Californian grapefruit, lavender, bergamot, tangerine
Middle notes
Pepper, coriander
Base notes
Oakmoss, ambergris, patchouli

House	Czech & Speake
Date	1993
Perfumer	unknown

Character

At last, a grapefruit smell that is clean, true to the fruit and enduring; deepening into a subtle, smoky sexiness without ever becoming heavy.

Story

The Seri Indians call grapefruit 'sahmees hamt cahaacol' which means 'orange that enlarges the breast'. Only, I would have thought, if you put them down your sweater. Grapefruit is a natural mutation of the pomelo, first described by Griffity Hughes on his trip to Barbados in 1750. He called it the forbidden fruit. Czech & Speake are a British company who make elegant bathroom equipment and accessories, as well as a line of eaux de toilettes and soaps.

Ô de Lancôme

Character

Citrus overture rounded with green herbs and a gently played rose-jasmine accord. Three new ingredients have been added: grapefruit, water lily, and an astringent splash of witch hazel. The base is cool, woody and dark green with a chypre timbre. Beautifully balanced; quiet.

Story

A classic eau fraîche, a composition which has the citrus theme of an eau de Cologne (see 4711 p. 97), and, in this case, some of the herbs as well, but with a more floral heart. Ô de Lancôme was a success from its launch in the days of the Paris students' revolution. Still packaged in its vintage frosted bottle with its design motif like 1960s wallpaper.

Top notes

Bergamot, lemon, mandarin, petitgrain, basil, grapefruit, witch hazel

Middle notes

Rosemary, coriander, honeysuckle, jasmine, rose, water lily

Base notes

Oakmoss, sandalwood, vetiver

House	Lancôme
Date	1969
	updated 1995
Perfumer	René Gonon

Eau de Cologne Impériale

Top notes

Bergamot, lemon, rosemary

Middle notes

Neroli, verbena

Base notes

There are none

Company	Guerlain
Date	1853
Perfumer	Pierre François-Pascal Guerlain

Character

Invigorating but delicate – a feminine eau de Cologne. The bergamot mellows the lemon and the hint of rosemary, then melts into the heavenly smell of neroli – distilled from the flowers of the bitter orange tree.

Story

People often assume that fresh, clean scents are a modern phenomenon, but in the nineteenth century, heavy notes were considered vulgar; and light, limpid perfumes were favoured. Impériale was created for the Empress Eugénie of France, wife of Napoleon III. She loved it so much that she appointed Guerlain court perfumers. Henceforth the Impériale bottle was studded with the imperial Napoleonic bee. A special bottle can be ordered with bees of real gold and embossed with your name.

Special No. 127

Character

Radiant orange blends with limpid roses. Sweet, gentle neroli in the heart. This perfume is discreet on a great-aunt, demure on her great-niece.

Story

Created for the Russian Grand Duke Orloff during his exile in Paris (men wore more feminine scents in the nineteenth century), this perfume was originally known as Orloff Special, then renamed after the Duke's death for the page it occupies in Floris's formula book. Eva Perón was a devotee. Floris is one of the oldest perfume houses still in existence. Begun in 1730 by the Spanish-born Juan Famenias Floris, it is still housed at 89 Jermyn Street in London, round the corner from the court of St James. The mahogany showcases in the shop were acquired from the Great Exhibition of 1851.

Top notes	
Rose, orange, petitgrain	
Middle notes	
Neroli	
Base notes	
Patchouli	

House	Floris
Date	1890
Perfumer	James Bodenham

Neroli Sauvage

Top notes	
Bergamot, petitgrain, lemon, grapefruit, orange bigarade	
Middle notes	
Neroli, orange flower, verbena	
Base notes	
Sandalwood, ambergris	

House	Creed
Date	1994
Perfumer	Olivier Creed

Character

From their Millesime range (a term that denotes quality), Neroli Sauvage (wild neroli) is intended for men, but it's great on a woman. Clean, zestful, with a delicate floral heart of neroli (bitter orange flower) and a subtly sensual drydown that enhances the skin's own aroma.

Story

Creed is a rarity. Started in 1760 by James Henry Creed in London, it is still family-owned today under its president and perfumer, Olivier Creed. His son is now studying perfumery in Grasse, and will one day take the helm. Creed was the official perfumer to Queen Victoria's court, then to the courts of Spain, France and Austro-Hungary. In 1854, under the patronage of Empress Eugénie, it moved to Paris, where it remains today. The house still use traditional infusion techniques and hand-make all their scents.

Philosykos

Character
Like biting into a sun-ripened fig. First there is the sharp green of the outer skin, then the garnet warmth of the heart. Subtly sexy on bare skin.

Story
Diptyque are a deserved cult, not just for their eaux de toilettes, but for their candles, each of which smells precisely of one particular thing (the first to do so), and for their charming shop at 34 boulevard Saint-Germain in Paris. Desmond Knox Leet, who created many of the scents, was an Englishman brought up in France and also a fine painter. The shop continues to be run by his partner, Yves Coueslant.

Top notes	
Coriander, pepper, galbanum, blackcurrant buds	
Middle notes	
Fig leaves, coconut	
Base notes	
Fig, styrax, white cedar	

House	Diptyque
Date	1996
Perfumer	Desmond Knox Leet

Mûre et Musc

Top notes	
Orange, lemon, mandarin	
Middle notes	
Blackberry, red fruits, lily of the valley, hedione	
Base notes	
Musky notes, sandalwood (eau de parfum only)	

House	L'Artisan
Date	1978
Perfumer	Jean Laporte

Character
Individual. The blackberry note (mûre) smells succulent and natural with tingling, sherbety hesperidic top notes of orange, lemon and mandarin. The base is discreetly sensual musk.

Story
The perfumes from this small French house are olfactory treasures, free of vulgarity and chemical taint. They often evoke another age, with names like L'Eau des Merveilleuses, named for a group of aristocrats who, during the French Revolution, tied red ribbons around their throats to jest at death by guillotine. Mûre et Musc is their best-selling scent.

All About Eve

Character

The fun top note smells more like an apple-scented fizzy drink than anything Eve could have got her hands on.

Story

Sin strikes again in scent form, this time in a fragrance with a name reminiscent of light-hearted 1930s perfumes. All About Eve, in its stylized apple, was inspired by the first female. German designer Wolfgang Joop, whose scent it is, says: 'She was Adam's ideal companion, the perfect lover, mother and wife. Yet, as with all women in my life I've ever loved, she was also mysterious. Eve was ambitious, scheming, maybe even a little greedy.' Nobody's perfect.

Top notes	
Green and red apple	
Middle notes	
Cinnamon, jasmine	
Base notes	
Vetiver, vanilla	

House	Joop!
Date	1996
Perfumer	panel at Créations Aromatiques

Acqua di Giò

Character

Abruptly green, almost like spearmint chewing gum, then a daiquiri of virtual fruits with piercingly sweet, sharp floral hits and hints of crushed grapes. A 'sea spray' accord gives an aqueous note.

Story

Scents like this, bursting with fruits and with the obligatory 'watery' note (actually more like a form of fragrance air-conditioning) will go down as peculiarly typical of the mid-1990s. In a business that's traditionally all about attraction, they are oddly sexless, a refreshing trait. Scent psychologist Joachim Mensing has called these fruit notes 'upbeat, out of recession notes'. As a group, they remind me of kitsch Japanese erasers, fragranced to make them more attractive to under-tens.

ACQUA DI *Giò* DE GIORGIO ARMANI

Top notes	
'Sea-spray', green leaves, pineapple, plum, peach, grapefruit, marigold, lemon	
Middle notes	
Freesia, grape, jasmine, hyacinth, cyclamen, lily of the valley, carnation, ylang-ylang	
Base notes	
Musk, sandalwood	

House	Giorgio Armani
Date	1995
Perfumer	panel at Firmenich

Chloë Innocence

Character

A girlish composition with cut grass and green apples against a watercolour background of shimmering flowers and fruits. Like an English summer.

Story

Unfairly unsung, this is a charming scent, very different in character from the original Chloë (see p. 60). The milky glass bottle by Fabian Baron captures light so that it seems to be blushing. Since the scent's launch, designer Stella McCartney, daughter of Beatle Paul, has revived the fashion house with her youthful London style.

Top notes

Apple, green notes, bergamot, peach, water hyacinth

Middle notes

Freesia, honeysuckle headspace, lily of the valley, violet

Base notes

Cedarwood, vetiver, heliotrope headspace, musk

House	Chloë
Date	1997
Perfumer	Natalie Lorson

Polo Sport Woman

Top notes

Tangerine, Sicilian lemon, pineapple, Sicilian bergamot, exotic fruit accord, spearmint

Middle notes

Brazilian rosewood, Jamaican ginger, nutmeg, orange flower

Base notes

There are none

House	Ralph Lauren
Date	1995
Perfumer	panel at Mane

Character

Once again, the familiar fuzzy exotic fruit accord of the 90s, with an aqueous, ozonic feel.

Story

It was Jean Patou in the 1920s who said the French woman is Venus, the American, Diana. Diana, Roman goddess of the hunt, was the presiding deity of female athletes. While this may no longer be accurate it holds for the world of fragrance advertising. While the French continue to show images of women as Venus (see Givenchy's Organza p. 118), or, if they have her outside, show her lying comatose in the sand (see Dune p. 134), America has embraced the light, bright sports scent with its images of woman as the victor in competitions other than the sexual one.

Calyx

Character

Uplifting, sparkling, totally tropical and with a grapefruit accent though there's no actual grapefruit. There's a brief instant of almost durian-fruit weirdness in the top note. Interesting raspberry in the base.

Story

The first tropical fruit fragrance, mother to a 90s megatrend. 'Some fruit accords, like the one in Calyx, have a very pure quality', says its creator, Sophia Grojsman. 'It's a different kind of sexuality, more innocent than the animal notes. . . . And men like innocence. To them it is sexy. . . . Fruit also carries a connotation of sin. Where would Adam and Eve have been without that apple?'

PRESCRIPTIVES CALYX

Top notes	
Mandarin, peach, passionfruit, mango, papaya, guava, apricot, spearmint, bergamot	
Middle notes	
Freesia, rose, lily of the valley, neroli, jasmine, marigold	
Base notes	
Oakmoss, raspberry, sandalwood, vetiver	
House	Prescriptives
Date	1986
Perfumer	Sophia Grojsman

Sunflowers

Top notes	
Lemon, neroli, melon, mandarin, rosewood, green note	
Middle notes	
Cyclamen, lily of the valley, jasmine, orris, rose	
Base notes	
Cedar, musk, oakmoss	
House	Elizabeth Arden
Date	1993
Perfumer	David Apel

Character

A summer scent with an excellently balanced top note of sharp lemon sherbet softened by melon with a tinge of orange blossom and the coolness of rosewood. Powdery mid-note; surprisingly warm – but faint – base. The overall impression is of a bright, upbeat spritz.

Story

Just what women wanted after the big 'kiss kiss bang bang' perfumes of the 1980s. Sunflowers epitomized the trend for light, zestful scents with a soft, watery feel – here achieved with melon.

Cool Water Woman

Character

Like a pastel-tinted fruit jelly, it smells juicy and cherubically innocent. Hold out, though, for the gripping, if faint, whiff of fresh groin in the base.

Story

Like the earlier Eau d'Issey, Cool Water Woman's theme is the purity of water. It is the sister fragrance of Davidoff Cool Water, the men's scent with the memorable ad of the hunk who has dozed off in the surf at sundown. Davidoff is a cigar company – so what are they doing launching a fragrance that's all about cleanliness, vigour, ozone-rich air and, as Davidoff put it, 'the world's most beautiful bodies of water'? Reminiscent of a bottle of mineral water, the flacon encapsulates a droplet of glass.

Top notes
Quince, blackcurrant, pineapple, melon, ozone
Middle notes
Lotus, water lily, rose de mai, jasmine, peach, mulberry
Base notes
Orris, vetiver, sandalwood

House	Davidoff
Date	1997
Perfumer	Pierre Bourdon

Escape

Character

Light, suave floral-fruity fragrance with a slight spicy note of carnation and clove. Gentle, chaste and introspective.

Story

The urge to escape from the 80s urban, success-driven values into the cocoon of nature at the beginning of the 1990s was expressed both by ozonic scents such as Aramis New West, and demure, pastel florals with uplifting fruit notes like Calvin Klein's Escape. The elegant pepper-pot bottle was inspired by an antique flacon in Kelly Klein's collection.

Top notes
Chamomile, apple, lychee, ylang-ylang, French marigold, coriander, hyacinth, blackcurrant, mandarin
Middle notes
Jasmine, rose, osmanthus, plum, peach, clove, carnation
Base notes
Musk, sandalwood, tonka bean, vetiver

House	Calvin Klein
Date	1991
Perfumer	panel at Mane

Iceberg Twice

Character

If it were a work of art, it would be by Jeff Koons – screaming kitsch. Bouncy rubber fruits and relentlessly sweet, hi-energy flowers eventually deflate to a green-accented drydown. Dysfunctional.

Story

From the commercially successful Italian fashion house. Various well-known designers have done stints at Iceberg. Originally the line took inspiration from cartoon characters like Tweety-Pie and it's still got a youthful poppy edge. Rap artist Lil' Kim appeared in ads for the clothes in 2000.

Top notes

Melon, peach, aldehydes, 'water fruits', French marigold

Middle notes

Lily of the valley, gardenia, violet, lily of the valley, jasmine

Base notes

Musk, sandalwood, honey, amber

House	Iceberg
Date	1994
Perfumer	unknown

Hugo Woman

Character

A 'get out of bed' smell that kicks off with spangly fruits whizzed up with mint and basil. The next phase is watery, sweet cantaloupe melon, peach and what smells like papaya but apparently is papaya flower headspace. The floral mid-note is nicely balanced against spices and lavender. The base is warm with vanilla. A likeable perfume.

Story

Hugo Boss is a menswear range from Germany which made its first foray into fragrance with Hugo for Men and its well-known ad-line 'don't imitate – innovate'. The women's spritz has a similar philosophy. The brief given to the perfumer was 'the essence of individual identity'. Bit of a tall order.

Top notes

Mint, basil, cyclamen, cantaloupe, Granny Smith apple, papaya flower headspace, berries, peach

Middle notes

Jasmine, hyacinth, lily, orris, clove, sage, lavender

Base notes

Benzoin, amber, cedar, sandalwood, pine, vanilla

House	Hugo Boss
Date	1997
Perfumer	Ursula Wandel

Happy

Character

Yes, it's a happy smell. A zingy, initial burst of grapefruit and bergamot, with emollient melony tones and transparent flowers in the heart. Several notes with aptly 'happy' names like morning dew orchid and Hawaiian wedding flower are used here for the first time.

Story

Clinique, the American skincare company owned by Lauder, wanted to capture the positive mood they detected in the air after the gloom of grunge. They also usefully inform us that according to the World Values Survey, Icelanders are the happiest people in the world.

Top notes	
Ruby red grapefruit, bergamot, mandarin blossom, laurel	
Middle notes	
Boysenberry flower, morning dew orchid, melati	
Base notes	
Hawaiian wedding flower, lily, magnolia, mimosa	

House	Clinique
Date	1997
Perfumer	Roy Matts

Ô Oui

Top notes	
Bergamot, clementine, water hyacinth, nectarine, freesia	
Middle notes	
Pear, pineapple, honeysuckle, stephanotis	
Base notes	
Lily, 'frosted musk'	

House	Lancôme
Date	1998
Perfumer	Harry Frémont

Character

O non. Those familiar fuzzy fruits of the 1990s – again. Warm, tropical and unfolding into a high-pitched sweetness, Ô Oui has none of the crisp greenness of its big sister, Ô de Lancôme.

Story

Designed as a modern take on their 1960s classic, Ô de Lancôme, this one is directed, say Lancôme, at 'Generation O'. ('A generation who give a resounding "Yes!" to love, to laughter, to happiness and to the future.') Fuzzy fruit notes are supposed to be uplifting smells associated with happiness, hence they entered the 1990s as an antidote to recession doldrums. Then they stayed . . . and stayed . . . and overstayed.

Eden

Character

Tartly green introduction melts into a pleasant smell of fruit jellies with a tarragon tang. The flowers in the mid-note are pastel-soft, partly due to the effect of melon. You can detect the hawthorn-like note of acacia. Sensual but underplayed base note. A clean 'good morning' smell.

Story

Eden, Eve, serpents, apples and sin have always been a well-mined source for fragrance 'concepts'. This one focuses less on the sin aspect, and more on the prelapsarian bliss of simply meandering through the original garden, sniffing it all in. The opaline green glass bottle, like the others by Cacharel, is designed by Annegret Beier.

Top notes

Bergamot, lemon, green note, mandarin, tarragon, pineapple, melon

Middle notes

Water lily, lotus, acacia, mimosa, violet, tuberose, lily of the valley, jasmine, rose

Base notes

Cedar, patchouli, musk, vanilla, sandalwood

House	Cacharel
Date	1994
Perfumer	Jean Guichard

Flirt

Top notes

Dossinia, 'iced pomegranate', dewy leaves

Middle notes

Ginger flower, magnolia, lime blossom

Base notes

Tamboti wood, cashmerande

House	Prescriptives
Date	1998
Perfumer	unknown

Character

Melony overture with pomegranate and other fruit ices soon blends with a warm, caramely note of vanilla and cashmerande. The heart is tu xiang hwa or ginger flower – which smells quite gingery and the gentle freshness of lime blossom (tilleul). This is Calyx's little sister with a nod to Aramis New West.

Story

Prescriptives claim first use of the Chinese ginger flower and offer us this fable: 'Bao Lin, a Chinese princess, was sent to Tibet to marry against her will. She was given ginger roots by her lover on departure. As she travelled to her new destiny, her tears fell upon the roots and beautiful delicate flowers bloomed. The ginger flower has since become the symbol of undying love.' What I don't understand is, why say goodbye to the love of your life with a couple of ginger roots?

Il Bacio

Character

A cascade of succulent fruits with the aqueous overtones of melon. Osmanthus adds an apricot tint. The overall cuddly effect of all these edibles with demure flowers is pricked by an intriguing peppery backnote.

Story

Means 'the kiss' in Italian. An offshoot from the upmarket Borghese skincare line. The bottle cap is a type of love-knot also known as the Herculean or reef knot, that dates back thousands of years. It was commonly used as a symbol of the unbreakable bonds of eternal love in Roman jewellery.

Top notes

Freesia, lily of the valley, bergamot, mandarin, lemon

Middle notes

Melon, peach, cassis, rose, honeysuckle, osmanthus, plum, passionfruit, pear, cyclamen, jasmine, cattleya orchid, orris

Base notes

Cedar, musk, violet leaves

House	Borghese
Date	1993
Perfumer	Givaudan Roure

Tommy Girl

Character

Tommy Girl contains notes 'inspired by American wildflowers' such as Cherokee rose and Dakota lily. An exciting new fragrance concept? Relax yourself. It's 90s fragrance no. 2: exotic fuzzy fruits – again. Think blackcurrant buds and dewberry.

The saccharine-sweet florals at the heart are par for the course with this type of fragrance, softened with an aqueous melon-like accord. A pleasant, well-balanced example.

Story

The first women's fragrance from the all-American designer beloved by hip hop posses and clean-living college girls alike, marketed for him by Aramis.

Top notes

Mandarin, tangerine, spearmint, blackcurrant buds, dewberry, peach, marigold

Middle notes

Apple blossom, honeysuckle, violet, Dakota lily, Cherokee rose, freesia

Base notes

Cedar, sandalwood, musk, amber

House	Tommy Hilfiger
Date	1997
Perfumer	unknown

So Pretty

Character

A brief instant of out-of-control sweetness is soon followed by the brilliance of a summer fruit bowl. Some of the fruits (peach) smell plump and natural. Others, like the dewberry, have an unsubtle, synthetic feel. Upbeat, could be a bit cloying.

Story

As Pierre Rainero, director of communications at Cartier, the French jewellers, explains: 'The idea of the woman a scent is intended for exists before the fragrance, before the bottle, before the name.' And they had a remarkably precise vision of that woman: '25 to 30, dynamic, and can be sophisticated in a natural way.' To Pilar Boxford who helped shape the concept, 'she's chic but modern. She feels "so pretty" and is not afraid to express it.' Never let a marketing spin put you off a perfume.

Top notes	
Mandarin, neroli, peach	
Middle notes	
Jasmine, dewberry, centifolia and damascene roses, orris	
Base notes	
Vetiver, sandalwood	

House	Cartier
Date	1995
Perfumer	panel at Givaudan Roure

Diesel Plus Plus Feminine

Top notes	
Bergamot, passionfruit, green leaves, fantasy fruit note	
Middle notes	
Lily of the valley, jasmine, milk	
Base notes	
Vanilla, musk, tonka bean, sandalwood	

House	Diesel
Date	1997
Perfumer	panel at Marbert

Character

Is milk a smell you'd want to put behind your ears? According to the Japanese, Westerners smell of old rancid fat – a legacy of our dairy-rich diet. Luckily, this smells more of fluorescent rubber fruits.

Story

From the Italian street clothes company with the ultra-kitsch ads comes this fragrance, mystifyingly based on the 'pure qualities of milk'. The packaging is a cute Tetrapack milk carton, embossed with cows. Inside is a milk bottle with a dinky, white rubber cap. Launched with Diesel Plus Plus Masculine, the idea being to choose according to whether you're feeling more masculine or feminine that day.

Giò

Character

Surreal fruits, potent flowers. Densely sweet, almost like fruity toffee, but with a mitigating airy note in the background.

Story

Giorgio Armani is the Italian designer who invented the soft-shouldered 'feminized' version of the masculine tailored suit. The bottle is a representation of this shape. Giò is the short, nickname version of Giorgio pronounced Joe.

Top notes

Bergamot, mandarin, peach, marigold, violet, hyacinth

Middle notes

Tuberose, ylang-ylang, cassis, rose, jasmine, carnation

Base notes

Sandalwood, vanilla, musk, cedar, amber

House	Giorgio Armani
Date	1992
Perfumer	Françoise Caron

Poême

Top notes

Cassis, peach, bergamot, mandarin, orange flower, plum

Middle notes

Jasmine, freesia, tuberose, ylang-ylang, mimosa

Base notes

Vanilla, amber, tonka bean, musk

House	Lancôme
Date	1995
Perfumer	Jacques Cavalier

Character

Like ODing on rosehip syrup. Poême is a typical 1990s megadose of cassis with plum and peach for good measure. At this strength, the cassis is almost medicinal. Vanilla base.

Story

Lancôme wanted to do a fragrance based on flowers, combining fantasy notes of a snow flower – the Tibetan blue poppy – and a desert flower – the datura (see Secrete Datura p. 30). French Oscar-winning actress Juliette Binoche is the 'face' of Poême. At the launch at Le Moulin Rouge in Paris she strode on-stage and recited Baudelaire. Then Charles Aznavour sang.

Baby Doll

Top notes	
Grapefruit, redcurrant, rhubarb, pomegranate, grenadine	
Middle notes	
Rose, freesia, peach	
Base notes	
Ginger, cardamom, cinnamon, cedar	

House	Yves Saint Laurent
Date	1999
Perfumer	Cecile Matton

Character

Sexy and tacky like a gum-popping Lolita in pink satin hotpants. Bubblegum and tart cyberfruits fizz off your skin first; peach dominates the heart. The base is warm with caramely vanilla sugar and a pinch of spice. Olfactory candyfloss. Other scents along these lines have cloyed, but Baby Doll pulls it off. For 'Hello Kitty' fans.

Story

This is a bottled version of the late 90s fad for all things girlie – very post-post-feminist. 'Baby Doll likes surprises. Baby Doll has a sweet tooth' cooed the press release which came with 'My very own alphabet'. E was for electronic-techno music, A for amour, and K for 'kawaii', Japanese for 'cute'. The only kitsch scent from a very grown-up designer.

Byblos

Top notes	
Mandarin, grapefruit, peach, marigold	
Middle notes	
Cassis, mimosa, gardenia, honeysuckle, jasmine, ylang-ylang	
Base notes	
Raspberry, vetiver, pepper, musk	

House	Byblos
Date	1990
Perfumer	Illias Ermenidis

Character

Hot, simmered fruits dominate, thanks to peach and the cassis prevalent in so many late 1980s/early 1990s bouquets. Marigold essential oil, too, has a dense fruity odour. But it gets interesting in the base notes when raspberry rubs against pepper and musk. It's like the pudding called Strawberries Romanoff where strawberries and cream are sprinkled with black pepper. Weird but delicious.

Story

Byblos are an Italian ready-to-wear company who were a huge success in the 1970s. The house is named for the city in ancient Phoenicia which as early as 3200BC was the centre for exporting cedar of Lebanon to Egypt for use in perfumery, mummification and religious rites.

Jungle

Character

Deliciously different, and not for everyone, Jungle is a hot posset of warm spices and tangy fruits like prune, pineapple and mango. You'll detect caraway, clove, cinnamon and cardamom and then sticky vanilla in the base.

Story

A bit of a mish-mash of ideas. The press release tells us it's inspired by an imaginary jungle 'where an eternally youthful Kenzo plays Mowgli the magician'. The elephant on the bottle cap is, says Kenzo, 'my favourite animal. It is a god, and it brings me good luck.' He was inspired by nature, but also by the urban jungle and – computers. And by the way, this is, apparently, a 'New Age' scent. Maybe it's more a memento of Jungle Jap, his first boutique, which had walls painted with jungle images.

Top notes	
Mandarin, cardamom, prune, nutmeg, pineapple	
Middle notes	
Clove, caraway, cinnamon, ylang-ylang, mango, heliotrope, rose, bay, jasmine	
Base notes	
Liquorice, vanilla, patchouli, cashmerande	

House	Kenzo
Date	1996
Perfumer	Jean Louis Sieuzac and Dominique Ropion

Yohji

Top notes	
Green note, galbanum, linalool, mandarin, pineapple, cassis	
Middle notes	
Praline, raspberry, jasmine, lily of the valley freesia, azalea	
Base notes	
Vanilla, musk, benzoin, sandalwood, coumarin	

House	Yohji Yamamoto
Date	1996
Perfumer	Jean Kerleo

Character

Eccentric sweet perfume that interplays boldness and softness. It bursts open with punchy, herbaceous green notes, swiftly underlined with sugared fruits and a peppery tang. The drydown is sharp, quite aggressive and synthetic. Azalea absolute is included for the first time in a perfume.

Story

Japanese Yohji Yamamoto is a designer's designer who loves to play with draping and proportion, usually in a muted palette. Widely considered a fashion genius, he never conforms and nor does this powerful perfume, made for him by Patou's in-house perfumer, Jean Kerleo.

The
herbaceous
Family

Chapter 3

Typically these scents are packed full of
green notes herbs such as rosemary, mint,
sage, lavender and plant essences like
cucumber. Herbs were a traditional
component of eaux de toilettes and eaux
de Colognes, often used as medicinal
rubs as well as fragrances. They tend to
be invigorating as well as cooling; ideal in
summer or to purify a stuffy environment.
Nowadays they can also include woodland
ferny smells and even the scent of
wet, spring earth. These are light and
airy fragrances.

Bobbi

Character
Green citrus and leafy top notes with a cucumber wateriness dominating the heart. Herbaceous, cool, woody and reminiscent of Clinique's Wrappings.

Story
Bobbi Brown is the make-up artist who launched her own range with a collection of ten brown-toned lipsticks she sold out of a bag at Bergdorf Goodman, not having been allotted even counter-space. Her philosophy was to sidestep fashion, and give women the colours that really worked to enhance their natural beauty. Her practical, working approach to make-up has seen global success, and the company is now wholly owned by Estée Lauder.

Top notes	
Lemon, bitter orange, green mandarin, bamboo leaf, ylang-ylang	
Middle notes	
Watery cucumber note, water lily, phlox, jasmine, osmanthus	
Base notes	
Sandalwood, Virginian cedar, orris, patchouli	

House	Bobbi Brown
Date	1998
Perfumer	Claude Dir

Cerruti 1881

Top notes	
Mimosa, freesia, bergamot, violet, aldehydes	
Middle notes	
Orange blossom, chamomile, geranium, jasmine, rosewood	
Base notes	
Sandalwood, cedarwood, amber, musk	

House	Cerruti
Date	1995
Perfumer	Claire Cain

Character
Airy, soft and herbal with camomile mid-notes and a clean woody residue of almost silky rosewood and cool cedar. Summery and highly wearable.

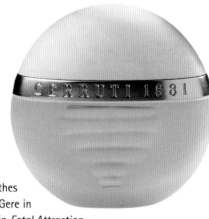

Story
Nino Cerruti is an Italian designer known for his menswear and the clothes he created for stars such as Richard Gere in *Pretty Woman* and Michael Douglas in *Fatal Attraction*. The company was started in 1881 by his grandfather as a textile firm. And it is a textile – linen – which has inspired this perfume. Linen, or flax flowers, do not actually have any aroma, but if they did, they might smell of the fresh accord of freesia, lily of the valley and aldehydes at the heart of this scent.

212

Character

Icy freshness cedes to lathery cleanness then a shower of luminous petals allied in a new accord with musk.

Top notes
Gardenia, bergamot, queen of the night cactus flower
Middle notes
Ghost white rosette, lily, lace flower
Base notes
Satinwood, sandalwood, 'halo musk lifescent'

House	Carolina Herrera
Date	1997
Perfumer	panel at Antonio Puig

Story

From Venezuelan-born New York socialite and designer Carolina Herrera, 212 is named for the Manhattan telephone code and inspired by the more downtown life of her daughter, Carolina Adriana. The bottle by Fabien Baron is ingenious: two metal globes that slot neatly into a glass and anodized metal docking device, so you can slip one in your bag and leave the other in your bathroom – or in your dressing room – depending on how downtown you are.

Route du Thé

Top notes
Green apple, tangerine, lemon, orange
Middle notes
Rose, jasmine, lily of the valley, peach
Base notes
Musk, amber

House	Barney's New York
Date	1984
Perfumer	unknown

Character

I'd heard this smelt of green tea. Green, certainly, but this is more the smell of an invigorating supermarket bubble bath than a cup of tea.

Story

A New York cult favourite from downtown department store – Barney's. The name means 'tea road' and is taken from an old Parisian salon du thé where the proprietress offered her customers her perfume samples along with their Lapsang.

Smell This

Top notes	
varies	
Middle notes	
varies	
Base notes	
varies	
House	Smell This
Date	1998
Perfumer	James Berard

Character

Definitely not for someone looking for a classic, romantic fragrance. Each little bottle aims to capture a smell-memory like a photograph would. For the young at heart.

Story

For the price of a cake, you can buy Cake Batter instead, with its yummy vanilla notes. Or Fluffy Pillow, with its starched odour of luxury hotel linen. My favourite, Canned Peaches, is like sticking your six-year-old nose into a can of Del Montes. 'Perfume sucks,' says perfumer James Berard. 'Perfume companies would like you to believe some superficial dream of looking like Kate Moss as you feel the sea breeze cross your face while caressing the most beautiful specimen of man. Screw that.' Instead he offers us scent-categories like 'Techno-Pop', 'Retro-Fume' and 'Scooby Snacks'. Musts: Head Shop, Boo-Boo Strips, Glue.

English Lavender

Top notes	
Lavender, rosemary, eucalyptus, bergamot	
Middle notes	
Spike lavender, clary sage, geranium, cedar	
Base notes	
Moss, tonka bean, musk	
House	Yardley
Date	18th century
Perfumer	unknown

Character

A Presbyterian female of unimpeachable virtue. And yet, how strange: for under the famous pristine effluvium, an almost chocolaty warmth slithers out for a moment, an odour more appropriate to Miss Jean Brodie.

Story

Lavender is a poetic smell that's due for a renaissance. The name comes from the Latin 'lavare' – to wash, and it has been used to scent fresh laundry since Roman times. The English house of Yardley dates back to 1770 and has always been known for its lavender waters. This is *Lavandula angustifolia,* commonly known as English lavender, grown in Norfolk, with its puritanical camphoraceous top note. The reproduction on the bottle is The Flower Sellers from *The Cries of London* by Francis Wheatley and dates from 1793.

Jicky

Character

On opening a bottle of Jicky, I sometimes smell petrol. Often described as
the first modern fragrance, it has the brutal beauty of a piece of modernist
architecture. The top notes are eau de Cologne-like, fresh herbs and citrus fruits
softened by lavender that segue into a sweet and woody heart note with
linalool – a new, at the time, synthetic isolated from rosewood. Throughout
there is the defining fougère or 'fern' note of coumarin, which smells of
new-mown hay.

Coumarin was isolated from the tonka bean in 1868. The third great
synthetic discovery in Jicky is vanillin. So far it could be a masculine fragrance
with a crystal-clear personality. But if you wait for the base notes, there is a
further surprise; hints of sensuality in civet, ambergris and musk still wrapped
in a soft cleanness. A great iconoclast, a great classic, and the dream perfume
for the woman who is tired of flowers.

Story

With Jicky, Guerlain became great, although
it had been in business since 1828. Aimé Guerlain,
son of the founder, enthusiastically embraced the
synthetics which have defined twentieth-century
perfumery. Jicky was supposedly named for a young
English girl he'd proposed to. It was also the
nickname of his nephew, Jacques Guerlain,
who went on to create classics such as
Shalimar and Mitsouko. Colette wore it.
In *Answered Prayers*, Truman Capote quotes
her: 'I like it because it's an old-fashioned
scent with an elegant history, and because
it's witty without being coarse – like the
better conversationalists.'

Top notes
Lavender, bergamot, lemon, mint, verbena, sweet marjoram, thyme, rosemary
Middle notes
Linalool, new-mown hay, sandalwood
Base notes
Amber, musk, civet, vanillin, tonka bean

House	Guerlain
Date	1889
Perfumer	Aimé Guerlain

Eau de Lavande

Character

Lavender is usually pretty much left alone to be polite and calming. But not here. This is the inspired love affair of clean, balsamic lavender and the sweet hay note in tonka beans plus vanilla with a little spice. The result is a kind of lavender chocolate and cigar smoke, and a whole new kind of sexiness. Created for men, destined for discerning women.

Story

Another work of startling simplicity from the Annick Goutal stable. With no resources and a fund of talent, the French Goutal launched into perfumery in the late 70s and produced a collection of distinctive scents quite unlike any others. Women who 'don't like fragrance' should try hers.

Top notes
Wild lavender
Middle notes
Pepper, clove
Base notes
Tonka bean, vanilla

House	Annick Goutal
Date	1981
Perfumer	Isabelle Doyen

Acqua di Parma

Character

Classic herby, slightly acrid cologne notes to open from which a sunny pairing of sweet and bitter orange emerges. Followed by a clean, almost soapy woodiness.

Story

This distinguished old cologne, once worn by everyone from Cary Grant to Ava Gardner, dates back to the 1930s but then nearly disappeared. It was rescued in 1994 by three Italian businessmen who loved it so much they bought the ailing business. Their first run was under a thousand bottles, many of them given to their friends. Since then, it's become a cult success with fashionable men and women all over the world. The bottle bears the crest of the Dukes of Parma, the Italian city which the scent comes from.

Top notes
Lemon, bergamot, English lavender, rosemary
Middle notes
Bitter orange, sweet orange, damascene rose, neroli, verbena
Base notes
Sandalwood, vetiver, patchouli, cedar

House	Acqu di Parma
Date	1930s
Perfumer	unknown

Etiquette Bleue

Top notes
Bergamot, orange, lemon, petitgrain, rosemary
Middle notes
Neroli, rosewood
Base notes
Sandalwood, balsam of Peru, oakmoss

House	D'Orsay
Date	1908
Perfumer	unknown

Character

A sunny, lively eau de toilette bursting with citrus fruits sweetened with their classic companion, neroli (light orange flower), on a gentle wood and moss base. For heatwaves.

Story

Comte Alfred d'Orsay, a supporter of Louis XVIII, was exiled to England during the Napoleonic years and met the beautiful – but married – Countess of Blessington. He won her heart, though she remained married, and loved her till he died. He married her stepdaughter, who, when she discovered his affair with her stepmother, deprived him of her fortune. He created this perfume for his love. The formula remained in the family vaults until 1908 when it was launched under the Compagnie des Parfums d'Orsay as Etiquette Bleue. Or so the story goes . . .

Eau Dynamisante

Top notes
Lemon, orange, thyme, rosemary
Middle notes
Caraway, ginger, coriander, lavender
Base notes
Patchouli, cardamom

House	Clarins
Date	1988
Perfumer	Jacques Courtin-Clarins with Clarins perfumers

Character

A high-energy blast of herbs and citrus like a classic male cologne. Settles to a sustained note of orange, lavender and spice. Prozac for the mind and a bull whip for sagging flesh.

Story

Up until the nineteenth century, scents were valued as much for their therapeutic properties as their odours. Scented plaguewaters and cure-alls were common, the most famous being the original eau de Cologne, still made under the name 4711 (see p. 97). Hungary Water, made for the Queen of Hungary in 1370, contained rosemary, marjoram, pennyroyal and, later, lavender and lemon. She was said to have been miraculously rejuvenated by it, receiving a marriage proposal from the King of Poland in her seventies. Eau Dynamisante does not promise royal proposals but it does contain many of the herbal ingredients found in these old colognes, as well as ginseng and ginger to tone the body, aloe to moisturize, and horsetail and Siberian ginseng to firm.

Bulgari Eau Parfumée & Extrême

Character

A pure, soothing scent and a deserved cult. If the very light Eau Parfumée vanishes too quickly for you, try the more concentrated Eau Parfumée Extrême, which has 15 per cent perfume oils as opposed to 4 per cent. They share a similar construction.

Opens with an iridescent citrus accord of bergamot (from the rinds of fruits of the bergamot tree) and bitter orange (from the rind of the Seville orange tree) together with lemon, and a tinge of green. You will detect more neroli, the blossom of the Seville orange tree, in the Extrême. The Extrême is also more suave due to rosewood and its high proportion of linalool.

Rose and jasmine are softly played in the mid-notes while the spices and tea begin to emerge, adding character. In the base, it's the wood notes, especially the unusual smoked woods that dominate while the tea lingers. The Eau is overall less about flowers and more about citrus, tea and wood. Generally, the feeling is celestial and fresh, mellowing into the more autumnal base notes. Eau Parfumée launched the trend for tea notes, and was aimed at both men and women ahead of cK one.

Story

Bulgari are a renowned Italian jewellers begun by a family of Greek silversmiths who emigrated in the mid-nineteenth century. They forged their signature style inspired by Greek and Roman classicism after the Second World War. Typically, their style combines classic stones and metals with more unusual substances such as haematite, mother of pearl and steel. All their perfumes are based on the theme of tea: there's a mother and baby line using camomile tea, Bulgari Parfum with jasmine sambac tea and Black (see p. 134) with lapsang souchong.

Top notes

Bergamot, lemon, green note, neroli (original: orange), (Extrême: rosewood, bitter orange)

Middle notes

Coriander, jasmine, damascene rose, green tea, pepper, cardamom, orris (original: lily of the valley)

Base notes

Smoked wood, cedar, sandalwood, oakmoss, tonka bean, beeswax, musk

House	Bulgari
Date	1992 and 1996 Extrême
Perfumer	Jean Claude Ellena

Paco

Character

Cool, balmy and leafy green. It opens with a happy marriage of crisp citrus and lavender against an aqueous background. Next there's a soft and herby tea note with just a little flower dust in the heart. Fresh, but sexy base with a lingering note of pineapple. Unusual splash.

Story

Launched as a 'fragrance for the people' Paco is a unisex spritz, introduced in the wake of cK one. It has several innovative features however: it comes in a recyclable aluminium can with no cap – a small metal clip attaches instead. It's sold in milk crate merchandizers with no box. And you get it in a plain paper bag, or, if you're lucky, from customized soft-drink dispenser machines at airports. Groovy.

Top notes	
Bergamot, lemon, mandarin, green note, coriander, lavender, pineapple	
Middle notes	
Tea, jasmine, geranium, cyclamen, orris	
Base notes	
Cedar, tonka bean, musk, amber, sandalwood	

House	Paco Rabanne
Date	1996
Perfumer	Rosendo Mateu

Eau Sauvage

Top notes	
Bergamot, lemon, petitgrain, basil, cumin	
Middle notes	
Hedione (from jasmine), lavender, patchouli, carnation, coriander, orris, sandalwood	
Base notes	
Oakmoss, vetiver, amber	

House	Christian Dior
Date	1966
Perfumer	Edmond Roudnitska

Character

The citrus top notes each seems to occupy its own separate airspace, balanced against basil, spicy coriander and cumin, an ingredient which has been compared to a woman's sweat. Eau Sauvage is famous for being the first scent to incorporate hedione or dihydrojasmonate, a synthetic isolated from jasmine absolute and smelling of the greener, fresher part of the flower. An aristocrat among perfumes.

Story

From its launch, this modern classic for men was avidly adopted by women, an appropriate move in the decade of Women's Liberation. The ads, sketched by René Gruau, added to its success. The 'eau sauvage' man was as much a hit then as Davidoff man is now; first appearing as just a pair of hairy legs under a bathrobe.

cK one

Character

'Jumping in the air, just showered after a warm day' is how Ann Gottlieb, who has art directed all of Klein's scents since Obsession, describes this one. Ideal as a sensuous, everyday splash.

Story

cK one was a phenomenon when it launched, selling in figures of biblical proportion and drawing a whole new customer, glamour-free kids like those in the ads, into department stores. It was not the first unisex fragrance – these go back to ancient times, or, more recently, to Jean Patou's Le Sien of 1929. But it was certainly a concept in tune with the 1990s. The bottle was created by then art director of *Harper's Bazaar*, Fabien Baron, and is based on a quarter bottle of Jamaican rum.

Top notes

Bergamot, lemon, mandarin

Middle notes

Hedione, (derived from jasmine), violet, rose, nutmeg

Base notes

Musk, amber

House	Calvin Klein
Date	1994
Perfumer	Alberto Morillas

Chakra V

Top notes

Orange, chamomile

Middle notes

Rose, geranium

Base notes

Cardamom, narcissus

House	Aveda
Date	1989
Perfumer	Koichi

Character

This is the perfume I kept dabbing on my throat throughout writing this book. I hope its effect on my writing was more creative than the actual smell, which, while not groundbreaking, is a pleasant citrus and spice accord with a hint of soothing rose-geranium. Pure and a little soapy.

Story

A very 1990s concept from natural beauty company, Aveda, now owned by Lauder. Aveda call their perfumes 'purefumes' instead of perfumes because the ingredients are 100 per cent naturally derived. Horst Rechelbacher, who began the company, told me once he believes essential oils have their own vibrational energy. The seven chakra scents are inspired by the Ayurvedic belief in seven chakras or energy centres in the body. Each scent supposedly helps balance the wavelength of a particular chakra.

CREATIVITY

CHAKRA™

V

PURE-FUME
SPIRIT™

AVEDA™

4711

Character

The classic eau de cologne. It's a great smell, stinging your nose with an explosion of citrus oils, then mellowing into a heart of sweet neroli and rose with soothing lavender. Dies away to a tinge of musk.

Story

4711 Echt Kôlnisch Wasser eau de cologne is an amazing survivor, valued for its aromatherapeutic properties as much as its smell. And what properties were claimed for it over the centuries: 'a miraculous antidote against poisons of all kinds', not to mention a dispeller of 'all hardened, tough slime'. Napoleon is said to have doused himself in a bottle a day and sucked sugar cubes dipped in it, crediting it with stimulating his brain. Seventy years later, composer Richard Wagner wrote: 'I expect to use about one litre [of eau de Cologne] a month; please send me three litres for one quarter, so we can see how we manage.'

Dispute surrounds its origin. 4711 was made until recently by the Muelhens family (now owned by Wella). The Muelhens claim the recipe was a wedding present from a Carthusian monk called Farina to young William Muelhens in Cologne in 1792. It was first known as 'aqua admirabilis', but by 1865 there were 39 manufacturers of Kôlnisch Wasser in Cologne, and all had the name Farina. The water may well have been brought to Cologne from Italy in 1694 by Giovanni Paolo de Feminis. He said the recipe had been given to him by a monk whose life he saved. The Feminis family made a fortune from it, before the formula passed to a nephew, Jean-Marie Farina in 1766.

In 1806, another Farina, also Jean-Marie, opened a shop in Paris, claiming to be related to this nephew. His formula was eventually acquired by Roger et Gallet in 1862 who launched their perfume house with it. The stories do not end. Another says that the original came from the Officina Profumo-Farmaceutica di Santa Maria Novella, founded in Florence in 1612 (and still there). The monks of the apothecary produced an Acqua della Regina, which was brought to Paris by Catherine de Medici, and copied by Paul Feminis. Yet another possibility is that it was developed in the 18th century by English military doctors in India to combat dysentery. 4711 refers to the street number of the Muelhens original shop.

Top notes	
Bergamot, mint, lemon, orange, petitgrain, neroli	
Middle notes	
Lavender, rosemary, rose	
Base notes	
Musk	

House	Muelhens
Date	1792
Perfumer	unknown

Lei

Character

Opens with cool, tangy herbs like a man's aftershave (but don't let that put you off). Dries down to subtle flowers and woods with a tinge of musk.

Story

So many scents have been launched as 'ze storee of un homme et une femme' but some are more flagrant 'storees' than others. Lei (she), was launched under Giorgio Armani's diffusion line, Emporio Armani, simultaneously with a man's version, Lui. 'He' is dark and matt. 'She' is pale gold and shiny. 'He' has a protuberance. 'She', an orifice. And would you believe it? The two slot neatly together. The rubber spray device contrasts in a fetishy way with the cold metal cylinder. Somehow, the spray action is incredibly sexy.

Top notes

Angelica, cardamom, yuzu, sage

Middle notes

Heliotrope, jasmine, vetiver

Base notes

Vanilla, cedar, musk, guaïacwood

House	Emporio Armani
Date	1998
Perfumer	Daniele Roche

Old Spice

Top notes

Orange, lemon, lavender, basil, petitgrain

Middle notes

Carnation, geranium, lily of the valley, orris

Base notes

Sandalwood, cedar

House	Shulton
Date	1937
Perfumer	William Lightfoot Schultz

Character

There's a bit of Old Spice in most men's fragrances, but the sophisticated, clean, smooth spiciness of the original is great on a woman too. Flower notes soften its heart, and woods add austerity.

Story

Once, I did a blind-test of fragrances with perfumers and women whose business involved smell. Nearly all agreed on one heavenly potion as the most expensive, feminine, sexy, sophisticated. In short, their favourite. When they took off their blindfolds, they saw it was – Old Spice. The lesson is: use your nose, not your eyes when choosing a scent. Just like the ad of 1969 says: 'Girls like it – Is there any better reason to wear Old Spice?' Famed for its 1970s surfer commercial set to *Carmina Burana*. A bestseller for 40 years.

Odeur 53

Character

Unusual mix of synthetics 'cloned from non-organic materials'. Refreshing contrast to the pretty-pretty flower fragrances of late 90s. Some items whose molecules were cloned: nail polish, metal, burnt rubber, mountain air and 'wash drying in the wind'. Smells more like a fresh cologne with a goodly dose of linalool Very fleeting.

Notes	
New non-organic synthetics	
House	Comme des Garçons
Date	1998
Perfumer	Anne Sophie Chapuis & Martine Pallix

Story

It's great to find a scent boldly named 'Odour' that comes in a squeaky metallic bag that you open like a packet of crisps. Kawakubo the Japanese designer behind Comme des Garçons says it's to 'create around you the smell that you like' rather than to scent yourself for others. Named for its 53 ingredients and described by Kawakubo as: 'an abstract, anti-perfume.'

Dirt

Notes	
Lemon balm, grasses, 5 varieties of clover, moss, barks, pine, oak and other woods and a secret mineral complex	
House	Demeter
Date	1996
Perfumer	unknown

Character

Who wants to smell like dirt? Everyone, it turns out, from Sharon Stone to 'Dirty Harry', Clint Eastwood. Dirt smells like dirt, the damp, fertile kind you want to plunge your hands in and rub all over your body. With a hint of crushed lemon balm. One of very few fragrances to contain minerals. Designed also to layer with other Demeter scents.

Story

Christopher Brosius, who worked at Kiehls Pharmacy, had the idea to launch a range based around single notes like Black Pepper, Cinnamon Toast, String Bean or Clematis Montana. Dirt is one of his best. Brosius came across a perfumer who had created a base that smelt of 'earth'. No regular perfume house wanted it. So Brosius snapped it up and a truly individual smell was born.

The Chypre Family

This family of fragrances is named for the original Chypre (Cyprus) created by famous perfumer François Coty in 1917. Coty's classic was based on the contrast between citrusy top notes and the pungent, earthy odour of oakmoss. All chypres are variations on this theme. They often include patchouli and woods, and ambery labdanum or animal notes. The heart note is floral. The overall impression is often powdery. Chypres can be womanly and alluring like Mitsouko, or quite cool and cerebral like Knowing, and thus ideal for wearing to work. A sophisticated group of perfumes.

Chanel No19

Top notes
Galbanum, neroli
Middle notes
Orris, rose de mai,
hedione (from jasmine)
Base notes
Cedar, oakmoss, vetiver,
leather

House	Chanel
Date	1970
Perfumer	Henri Robert

Character

Impossible to imagine No19 on a badly dressed woman. Green and powdery, its sensuality comes from its restraint. The green note is attenuated by neroli and hedione, the greener component of jasmine. Then velvety orris kicks in – lots of it. Woody base. Cool and warm at the same time.

Story

August 19th was Coco Chanel's birthday and this perfume was launched at Christmas 1970, a few months after her 87th birthday. It was to be her last creation. She died on January 10, 1971. It was Mlle Chanel's idea to do another perfume; Wertheimer, the company which own Parfums Chanel, were keen to preserve the aura around No5, and worried that a flop might affect it. But No19 was far from a flop. Overseen from beginning to end by Chanel, and based on a formula suggested by her, it is a very elegant success.

Cristalle

Character

Luminous, cold and abstract, and very like Diorella. But smell both together and you can see Cristalle is somewhere between Diorella and No19. Like a bouquet of lily of the valley chucked into undergrowth. I'm talking about the eau de parfum, created by Polge in 1993. It is fruitier and more vivacious in the eau de toilette.

Story

Launched a few years after Chanel's death. Would she have liked it? Does it matter?

Top notes
Bergamot, peach, lemon,
basil, cumin, hyacinth
Middle notes
Jasmine, melon, lily of
the valley, cyclamen,
narcissus
Base notes
Oakmoss, vetiver,
patchouli, musk, civet,
sandalwood

House	Chanel
Date	1974
Perfumer	Henri Robert/
	(eau de parfum)
	Jacques Polge

Diorella

Character

Few ingredients perhaps, but a complex character to this superb scent. It breaks open with the freshness of lemon and snapped leaves, then sinks into a heart of jasmine, but a light translucent jasmine, with a slight warmth of peach. Just a hint of chypre powderiness. The mood of the scent is cool, mathematical and twilit but with a curvaceous structure. Mysterious, it's a Mona Lisa among scents.

Story

Roudnitska said that Diorella was his proudest creation. If perfume is all about getting the ingredients in perfect proportion, he proved that less is more. Sadly only available in eau de toilette.

Top notes

Lemon, basil, bergamot, melon, green note

Middle notes

Peach, honeysuckle, jasmine, rose, cyclamen

Base notes

Oakmoss, vetiver, patchouli, musk

House	Christian Dior
Date	1972
Perfumer	Edmond Roudnitska

Aromatics Elixir

Top notes

Bergamot, green note, aldehydes, rosewood, palmarosa, coriander, chamomile

Middle notes

Rose de mai, jasmine, carnation, orris, ylang-ylang, orange flower

Base notes

Patchouli, vetiver, oakmoss, sandalwood

House	Clinique
Date	1972
Perfumer	panel at IFF

Character

Assertively powdery as only Ma Griffe is powdery, but more aromatic and 'fougère' than Ma Griffe. Like plunging through a ferny forest after a bath. Thrillingly strict and chilly.

Story

A sleeper success, loved besottedly by those who wear it. The first of several fragrances from the Lauder subsidiary skincare company. It has many ingredients chosen for their aromacological properties: rose de mai because it's toning and astringent, sandalwood and camomile for their traditional use in cleanliness, orange blossom because it's a relaxant. The name achieves the rare feat of mystery without cheesiness.

Coriandre

Character

A scent with a sylvan, crepusclar tonality due to the olfactory equivalent of a 'marriage of true minds' – coriander with murky patchouli, underscored with powder and wood. Cool, ferny and utterly sophisticated. For a red-headed Raymond Chandler heroine. Or an anchorite.

Story

Jean Couturier set up a perfume company to launch this fragrance which was created by his wife, Jacqueline, a Grasse-trained nose and the daughter and grand-daughter of perfumers. Re-jigged in 1993.

Top notes

Coriander, angelica, orange flower, aldehydes

Middle notes

Rose, geranium, jasmine, orris, lily, ylang-ylang

Base notes

Patchouli, oakmoss, vetiver, sandalwood, civet, musk

House	Jean Couturier
Date	1973
Perfumer	Jacqueline Couturier

Niki de Saint Phalle

Character

Opens like a pine forest, settling down to a tuberose-accented powdery chypre; clean and dry with lots of cerebral wood notes.

Story

Niki de Saint Phalle is a French sculptor famous for her massive female figures in bold patterns and colours, the 'Nanas'. She helped create the *jus* for this scent, and also designed the cobalt blue bottle with its lovemaking serpents. 'I chose serpents as the theme for my perfume because serpents are mysterious, erotic and sensual. And for me, the golden snake is the male and the female snake, of course, is the coloured one – the glorious one.'

Top notes

French marigold, lily of the valley

Middle notes

Ylang-ylang, tuberose, jasmine, vetiver, patchouli

Base notes

Moss, sandalwood, amber, musk

House	Niki de Saint Phalle
Date	1984
Perfumer	unknown

Halston

Top notes

Melon, green note, peach, bergamot, spearmint, marigold

Middle notes

Jasmine, rose, cedar, orris, ylang-ylang, carnation

Base notes

Moss, patchouli, vetiver, amber, musk, sandalwood, incense

House	Halston
Date	1975
Perfumer	unknown

Character

Acid and mint, then soapy. Segues into classic chypre powderiness with a rosy aura, then woody undertones. Very 1970s (compare with Rive Gauche see p. 47).

Story

The smell of Studio 54 from the American fashion designer who loved to party. Halston (born in Des Moines as Roy Halston Fronwick) created lean, fluid silhouettes stripped of extraneous ornament. Jewellery designer Elsa Peretti started out with Halston and went on to be the definitive 1970s jeweller with her organic silver jewellery for Tiffany. She designed this tactile bottle, typical of her style.

La Perla

Top notes

Carnation, freesia, osmanthus, tangerine

Middle notes

Coriander, pepper, cardamom, jasmine, damascene rose

Base notes

Patchouli, sandalwood, oakmoss, musk

House	La Perla
Date	1986
Perfumer	Pierre Wargnye

Character

This is a less powdery interpretation of the Coriandre rose-patchouli chypre accord with woody undertones. It's a well-rounded composition, neither too spicy nor too flowery. Slinky and soft.

Story

La Perla is a luxury Italian lingerie company, begun in 1954 by Ada Masotti, and still owned and run by the family. It is based in Bologna, a city known for its silk trade since the 16th century. La Perla's 'brief' to the perfumer was to create something seductive and intimate like silky lingerie. The connection between the intimacy of lingerie and scent had been made before. In 1925, Hermione Cadolle, who has a claim to have invented the first bra, launched Le No9 (still available, at Les Senteurs in London).

Knowing

Top notes

Coriander, aldehydes, bay, green note, orange, plum

Middle notes

Rose, jasmine, cardamom, pittosporum, lily of the valley, cedar, vetiver

Base notes

Patchouli, oakmoss, musk, amber, honey, civet

House	Estée Lauder
Date	1988
Perfumer	unknown

Character

Suave top note pierced by the angularity of aldehydes. Gives way to a take on the classic chypre poised between flowers and woody notes. Emphatically powdery and sisters with Aromatics Elixir, La Perla and Coriandre (see p. 103, p.104 and 105).

Story

Aimed at 1980s high-achievers, Knowing is, like many chypres, ideal for a working woman. Evelyn Lauder, wife of Leonard, Estée's son, smelt pittosporum while on holiday in the south of France. She tracked the odour down to the market in Cap d'Antibes. It became an element of this scent.

Calèche

Top notes

Bergamot, mandarin, neroli, aldehydes

Middle notes

Jasmine, rose, orris, lily of the valley, gardenia, ylang-ylang

Base notes

Vetiver, oakmoss, sandalwood, cedar, cypress, olibanum

House	Hermès
Date	1961
Perfumer	Guy Robert

Character

Orris and rose with the sparkle of aldeyhydes. Woody. A scent that sums up the meaning of 'good taste'. Calèche, resonates quietly. Unlike many more modern perfumes, it's not sickeningly sweet or heavily oriental. But certainly not old-fashioned.

Story

Hermès opened in Paris in 1837 selling bridles and harnesses, and by the 1960s had expanded to include the highest quality handmade leather goods. They are particularly renowned today for their 'Kelly' bags and silk scarves. Capitalizing on their image, they chose the name 'Calèche', a fine-lined type of carriage, said to be the most exquisite ever made. The carriage on the label, however, is not a calèche, but a grand duc, the Hermès trademark since 1945.

Ma Griffe

Character

Smell this and know what a chypre should be. Ma Griffe is the driest, most powdery of perfumes, a wonderful trait, though not for everyone. It's starkly green, thanks to galbanum, clary sage and an overdose of styrallyl acetate – a substance that is found naturally in gardenia buds. Ma Griffe is like a walk in a just-budding flower garden on a frosty day.

The aldehydes add sparkle, the citronellas and citrus oils a burst of tonic acidity. Jasmine and rose bring femininity to the mid-notes, but unlike so many scents, it's never more than slightly sweet. Styrax predominates in the base with its offbeat, cinnamon-like odour. Launched as a young scent, at a time when there were no fragrances for young girls, Ma Griffe now seems appropriate for a working woman. It smells tailored, smart and resonant with clarity. A true original.

Story

Born Carmen de Tomaso, Mlle Carven was not fond of her name, so she simply substituted for the 'm' each consonant of the alphabet in turn until she found one she liked: 'v'. She solved another frustration in an equally practical way. Petite to the point of minute, she found it difficult to get clothes that suited her. So she launched a couture house in 1945 geared to women who were similarly dainty. Ma Griffe was launched a year later. The name means both 'my signature'(in French, a designer's marque is called his 'griffe') and 'my talon'. To have someone in your griffes is to have them in your clutches. The scent was vibrantly different. Not a rich odalisque smell nor yet a pretty floral, its reverberating green powder dared to challenge the tastes of the time.

It was a great success, not least because of clever promotion techniques, unheard of at the time, like the parachuting of Paris with thousands of sample bottles. In her first collection, Carven showed a tight-waisted, full-skirted dress in green and white stripes called Ma Griffe. The green and white stripes of the packaging are taken from this.

Top notes
Gardenia, citronella, citrus, aldehydes, galbanum, clary sage
Middle notes
Jasmine, rose, ylang-ylang, orris, vetiver, sandalwood
Base notes
Styrax, oakmoss, benzoin, vetiver, labdanum, musk

House	Carven
Date	1946
Perfumer	Jean Carles

Diva

Character

A rich floral chypre, given roundness by tuberose and both the damascene rose of Turkey and the centifolia rose, grown in Grasse and Morocco. The flowers are enveloped in the soft, green balm of a woody background with lots of powdery notes and a hint of green spice. Cool and elegant, but ready to unzip its dress.

Story

Emanuel Ungaro is a French couturier known for his love of soft feminine drapes and floral prints. This, his first perfume, is centred on the rose, his favourite flower. He designed the bottle in conjunction with Jacques Helleu to suggest the pleated drapes of one of his dresses.

Top notes

Mandarin, aldeydes, coriander, rosewood, tuberose, cardamom

Middle notes

Damascene and centifolia roses, jasmine, narcissus, carnation, ylang-ylang

Base notes

Patchouli, sandalwood, oakmoss, honey, vetiver, civet, musk, labdanum

House	Ungaro
Date	1982
Perfumer	Jacques Polge

Charlie

Top notes

Citrus, peach, geranium, hyacinth, tarragon

Middle notes

Jasmine, rose, ylang-ylang, cyclamen, orris, lily of the valley

Base notes

cedar, sandalwood, oakmoss, vanilla, musk

House	Revlon
Date	1973
Perfumer	panel at Florasynth

Character

A soft, balsamic floral chypre, powdery and with a nuzzling warmth. Very pretty and wearable.

Story

Charlie was, in a way, the first feminist fragrance. In her pantsuit (a first, no woman in a scent-ad had worn one before), Charlie was the vision of the androgynous new woman stepping out to conquer the workplace – admired by men but never ruled by them. It was the first lifestyle fragrance. Young women bought it more to live like Charlie than to look or smell like her. In a way they were hoping it would work like magic – one spritz and the world would be their oyster. It was named for Charles Revson, owner of Revlon, and codenamed Cosmo while being developed, for the young, liberated *Cosmopolitan* readers it was aimed at. The face of Charlie was Shelley Hack of *Charlie's Angels* fame. It instantly became the top-selling, mass-market fragrance worldwide.

Deci Delà

Character

A gourmand feast of subtle fruit top notes with a complex chypre accent adding a cool, airy feel. There's a charming and original accent of hazelnut in the heart of spring flowers. Warm vanilla and balsam base.

Story

Nina Ricci was a couturier who opened her house in 1932. The name is most famous as the marque of the classic perfume L'Air du Temps (see p. 54). This scent, aimed at the young, comes in a bottle designed by Garouste & Bonetti, who also designed Lacroix's couture salon. The name means 'here and there'.

Top notes

Raspberry, watermelon, pawpaw, osmanthus, peach, boronia headspace, redcurrant

Middle notes

Rose, freesia headspace, sweet pea, hazelnut, papaya, orris, carnation

Base notes

Cypress, patchouli, sandalwood, vanilla, 'aquatic' oakmoss, cedar, styrax, benzoin, amber, musk, agarwood

House	Nina Ricci
Date	1994
Perfumer	Jean Guichard

Yvresse

Top notes

Nectarine, mint, aniseed, cumin, violet

Middle notes

'Blue rose', rose, lychee

Base notes

Vetiver, oakmoss, patchouli

House	Yves Saint Laurent
Date	1993
Perfumer	Sophia Grojsman

Character

Imagine fruit salad in eau de vie with crystallized violets on top. Then imagine having a bath in it. In the light version, though, nectarine flower replaces the fruit, blackcurrant leaves replace aniseed, mimosa replaces rose and white lilac replaces lychee. Sparkling, almost fizzy.

Story

Originally launched under the name 'Champagne' in its champagne cork bottle, this perfume got up the noses of the French champagne growers. When journalists arrived in Paris for the launch they were heckled by farmers smashing bottles of champagne. Later they watched the YSL President, Pierre Bergé, scuffling with the viniculturists. YSL lost its European court battle over the name and was obliged to change it. Yvresse is a play on the French word *ivresse*, meaning drunkenness, and Yves, Saint Laurent's first name.

Femme

Character

A deluxe French patisserie – all mille feuilles of hot, buttery pastry, peaches and prunes dusted with cinnamon and spun sugar. In Femme, even the bergamot top note smells dense. It soon blossoms with peach and earthy oakmoss, accented with a tenacious sugarplum note that develops through the whole structure. Fondant rose with jasmine, grown in Rochas' own fields in Grasse, dominate the heart. Lush, with the power to fill a room, and lasts for hours.

Story

Femme was the first major success of perfumer Edmond Roudnitska, the man who went on to create Diorissimo, Diorella, Eau Sauvage and Eau d'Hermès. He was working in Grasse during the war when Marcel Rochas, the couturier, came looking for a perfume. Roudnitska was reduced at the time to jobs such as finding a substitute for butter, due to the privations of war. But he gave Rochas the only scent he had: a tenacious fruity chypre. As he himself says: 'it was very gourmande, very patisserie' – a direction he later rejected. According to Michael Edwards' *Perfume Legends*, Roudnitska attributes Femme's sensuality to a methyl ionone compound that smelt of crystallized prunes. It had lain in a barrel in a corner of a courtyard at the factory for perhaps 20 or 30 years when Roudnitska dipped his nose in and was entranced. Femme was an instant success. Rochas offered it as a wedding present to his young, beautiful wife, Hélène, in 1944 and then made it available on subscription to Paris' chicest women – a move necessitated by the rationing of alcohol and glass, but it created an aura of exclusivity.

In 1945 he launched it to a wider audience with an exhibition 'Les Parfums à Travers la Mode 1765–1945'. Visitors to the exhibition could smell Femme in company with great scents of the past, but not those of his competitors.

The curvaceous bottle for Femme was inspired by Mae West's hips. Rochas had been to Hollywood to design costumes for the diva, often decorating them with black Chantilly lace. Femme originally came in a box wrapped in Chantilly lace. Today the box is printed with it. In 1989, Femme was relaunched and the *jus* revamped by Olivier Cresp of Quest. The essence had been adulterated over the years. Cresp steered it back to its roots and simplified the formula, adding a few accents such as an Indian curry note.

Top notes
Peach, prune, bergamot, cinnamon, aldehydes

Middle notes
Jasmine de Grasse, damascene rose, everlasting flower, ylang-ylang

Base notes
Amber, oakmoss, sandalwood, musk

House	Rochas
Date	1944
Perfumer	Edmond Roudnitska/ updated by Olivier Cresp

Mitsouko

Character

One day, in Paris, someone got into a taxi beside me smelling the way God intended women to smell: plush, troubling and golden. It was Mitsouko. Although it's a scent perfumers admire, it's not as well known to the public as Guerlain stablemates Shalimar and Samsara. But Mitsouko is a magnificent creation. Its secret is the harmony of the peach note with the earthiness of oakmoss. The golden warmth of ripe peach skins comes from an aldehyde, C-14, very different from the aldehydes used shortly thereafter in Chanel No5. But you could not describe it as fruity. Or flowery, or spicy, or animal. It's too beautifully balanced for one note to predominate. Ideal for a grown-up woman sure of her sensuality. Dreamy on many redheads.

Story

Mitsouko is a scent that's always implicated in sex. Jean Harlow wore it and her first husband killed himself after first dousing himself in a bottle of Mitsouko. They had only been married a week. Impotence drove him to it. Then in the film *Belle du Jour*, Catherine Deneuve smashes a huge bottle of it before setting off to spend the afternoon as a prostitute, returning to her rich husband in the evening. Men have been ensnared by Mitsouko too: Charlie Chaplin drenched himself in it and Diaghilev, the Ballets Russes impresario, sprayed it on his hotel curtains.

'Mitsouko' is Japanese for mystery, and the scent was launched after the First World War at a time when everything oriental was in vogue in Europe. Nowadays we think of the East as mystic. But then it was associated with languorous abandon making it a natural source of imagery for the sensuous perfumes coming into fashion. The name came from the heroine of a novel hugely popular at the time, Claude Farrère's *La Bataille* (The Battle). It was the story of the romance between a young British naval officer on board the flagship of the Japanese fleet during the war between Russia and Japan, and the admiral's wife, Mitsouko, also on board the ship. The bottle for Mitsouko is identical to that of another Guerlain scent, L'Heure Bleue (see p. 65) launched in 1912, due to the bottle shortage after the war.

Top notes
Bergamot, mandarin, neroli
Middle notes
Rose, jasmine, peach (aldehyde C-14), clove
Base notes
Oakmoss, labdanum, patchouli, vetiver, cinnamon

House	Guerlain
Date	1919
Perfumer	Jacques Guerlain

Montana Parfum de Peau

Character

A chypre with personality. The fruity green top note is punctured by hot pepper and cool cardamom. The flowers of the mid-note are enlivened with ginger and sandalwood. Powdery throughout. A half-domesticated animal skulks in the base note.

Story

Claude Montana is a French designer known for his scalpel-cut jackets. The bottle for this scent, by Serge Mansau, is unique. It was inspired by the swirling fall of a winged sycamore seed as seen by a strobe light.

Top notes

Green note, pepper, cassis, cardamom, peach, plum

Middle notes

Ginger, rose, carnation, sandalwood, jasmine, tuberose, ylang-ylang, narcissus

Base notes

Patchouli, castoreum, civet, vetiver, olibanum, musk, amber

House	Montana
Date	1986
Perfumer	unknown

Paloma Picasso

Top notes

Bergamot, lemon hyacinth, ylang-ylang, angelica, clove

Middle notes

Rose de mai, jasmine, lily of the valley, orris

Base notes

Castoreum, oakmoss, vetiver, patchouli, amber, civet, musk, cedar, tobacco, sandalwood

House	Paloma Picasso
Date	1984
Perfumer	Francis Bocris

Character

A strong scent for an assured woman. Paloma Picasso has the heavy sensuality of copious quantities of castoreum (from beavers) swaddled in roses and with a disturbing background note of patchouli.

Story

Strange that Paloma Picasso's perfume was codenamed Daphne No19. Paloma transcended being 'the daughter of Picasso' to become a jewellery designer. She took a strong personal hand in choosing this perfume and designing the bottle, based on earrings made of petrified palm wood she had created for Tiffany.

Jolie Madame

Character

A cursory inspection of this scent may remind you of an old lady's violet-scented talc. Pay attention, though, and you'll find a complex liquid goddess. First there's a top note of wild wormwood (artemisia) which gives a weird, pungent, herby accent that is masterfully blended with creamy gardenia. Coriander adds a spicy tinge, then a well-controlled fistful of flowers, ceding to a dry powderiness. Eventually, you'll get patchouli, animal castoreum and leather. By one of the first women perfumers of modern times.

Story

An olfactory explosive. Pierre Balmain, who had Cellier create several scents for him, opened his couture house in 1946. His clothes were architectural with an icy hauteur. Gertrude Stein and Alice B Toklas adored them.

Top notes

Wormwood, gardenia, bergamot, coriander, neroli

Middle notes

Jasmine, rose, orris, narcissus, tuberose

Base notes

Patchouli, castoreum, vetiver, civet, leather, moss, musk

House	Balmain
Date	1953
Perfumer	Germaine Cellier

Miss Dior

Top notes

Aldehydes, galbanum, bergamot, clary sage, gardenia, lavender

Middle notes

Jasmine, narcissus, rose, neroli, orris, lily of the valley, carnation

Base notes

Patchouli, oakmoss, labdanum, vetiver, sandalwood, leather, coumarin, tonka bean

House	Christian Dior
Date	1947
Perfumer	Paul Vacher

Character

A discreet, elegant, powdery chypre with a green and aldehydic top note mollified by gardenia and a heart of velvety flowers. A hint of leather in the base.

Story

In 1947, Dior presented his first collection, the 'New Look', to a storm of controversy. It featured a tiny waist, padded hips and yards of fabric in the voluminous skirts. Women went wild for it after the privations of war, but those unable to afford so much cloth literally tore the outfits off women in the streets. In the same year, Dior launched this, his first scent, named Miss Dior in tribute to his sister.

Cabochard

Character

An iconoclast for women as *cabochard* (headstrong) as its name. As it opens you imagine yourself thrashing through wet bracken with its sour, acid green while scraping your nails on an orange you've got in your pocket. A spicy note soon emerges, and from this slowly builds to majestic proportions, the smoky, sultry crackle of leather against a soft heap of powder. The longer this scent lasts, the smokier it gets. For dominatrixes – in the boardroom or in bed.

Story

Madame Grès was one of the greatest couturiers, draping silk jersey to give it the purity of fluted Grecian sculpture. Her real name was Germaine Emilie Krebs. She designed under the name Alix, using her husband's name, Grès, from the German Occupation of Paris. The leather note of Cabochard is due to isobutyl quinoline, a synthetic discovered in the 1880s and also used in Tabac Blond, Cuir de Russie and Bandit.

Top notes
Aldehydes, bergamot, mandarin, galbanum, spice note

Middle notes
Jasmine, damascene rose, geranium, ylang-ylang, orris

Base notes
Patchouli, vetiver, castoreum, oakmoss, musk, labdanum, sandalwood

House	Grès
Date	1959
Perfumer	Bernard Chant

Bandit

Top notes
Galbanum, orange, neroli, artemesia

Middle notes
Ylang-ylang, jasmine, rose, tuberose, orris

Base notes
Oakmoss, leather, patchouli, vetiver, civet, castoreum, myrrh

House	Robert Piguet
Date	1944
Perfumer	Germaine Cellier

Character

A masterful counterpointing of ardour and aloofness. A raw green top note is subsumed in the prickly powderiness of oakmoss. Against this strictness plays sultry leather, the rank swamp-grass of vetiver and patchouli, and rich flowers smelt at a distance.

Story

In 1944, as Paris was liberated, couturier Robert Piguet launched his 'bandit' collection in which the models, brandishing guns and knives, swaggered down the catwalk with hooded faces, emitting waves of this, his first fragrance. Bandit was formulated by the great nose, Germaine Cellier. Legend has it that in order to create it she took to stripping models of their panties as they exited the runway, burying her nose in them in the belief 'this was when they let out the best of their femininity'.

Cuir de Russie

Character

Like the leather interior of an old Rolls. Impregnated with the spice of sage and carnation and the narcotic sex of jasmine, then fanned by woods and balsam. Edmond Roudnitska once described a long-gone perfume as 'a beautiful flower snapped into a new leather handbag'. For me, that's what this is.

Story

From the creator of the world's most famous perfume, Chanel No5, and arguably his best creation. Beaux was Russian, fleeing to France in 1917 in the wake of the Bolshevik revolution. This was his tribute to the motherland.

Top notes
Orange flower, bergamot, clary sage
Middle notes
Carnation, orris, jasmine, rose, cedar, vetiver
Base notes
Leather, silver birch, juniper, tobacco, styrax, cedar

House	Chanel
Date	1924
Perfumer	Ernest Beaux

Tabac Blond

Top notes
Orange flower, linden
Middle notes
Jasmine, carnation, vetiver
Base notes
Cedar, civet, patchouli, leather, oakmoss

House	Caron
Date	1917
Perfumer	Ernest Daltroff

Character

Voluptuous leather envelopes the jasmine heart and the spicy clove smell of carnation. Dry, golden base. I particularly like the eau de toilette where acidulous and resinous fresh notes clash violently with the earthy leather. If you like a smooth scent, go for the *extrait*.

Story

Tabac Blond – 'blonde tobacco' – was a homage to the woman who smokes. It was inspired by the aroma of the tobacco smoked by English soldiers in France during the First World War. When it was launched in 1919 smoking was considered terribly chic, something flappers did. Nowadays, this is the only acceptable way to get your tobacco fix.

The
Oriental
Family

Oriental scents are rich and sultry, due to their high preponderance of base notes. Some orientals, especially those centred on animal notes like musk, castoreum, civet and ambergris are overtly sexy. On the whole they are strong and enduring, but if you usually fall for lighter fragrances, explore modern, transparent orientals such as Le Feu d'Issey, Tiempe Passate or Very Valentino. And you should consider masterpieces like Must de Cartier, where the notes are delicately balanced to give the impression of depth rather than heaviness. If you like vanilla scents, look at the gourmand orientals with their distinctive food notes like chocolate, caramel and milk.

Very Valentino

Character

Flowery, with evanescent bergamot and mandarin and a lingering note of succulent blackcurrant. A featherweight floriental that quickly vanishes.

Story

The advertising campaign, according to the Italian designer, 'is about feeling, about feeling'. And the feeling he has in mind? According to the print-ad it's a case of 'I'm feeling very Valentino'. Not an emotion many of us experience regularly. Maybe it's how it feels to be born the son of an electrical-appliance store-owner and end up dressing everyone from Jackie Onassis to Courtney Love? Whatever, Valentino is a master-couturier.

Top notes	
Magnolia, bergamot, lemon, lily of the valley	
Middle notes	
Jasmine, rose de mai, fantasy wood notes	
Base notes	
Sandalwood, musk, amber	

House	Valentino
Date	1998
Perfumer	Danielle Roche

Organza

Top notes	
Sap, bergamot, cassis, orange flower, rosewood	
Middle notes	
Gardenia, tuberose, honeysuckle, ylang-ylang, peony, mace, nutmeg	
Base notes	
Vanilla, amber, cedar, guaîacwood, sandalwood, orris, musk	

House	Givenchy
Date	1996
Perfumer	Sophie Labbe

Character

An ambery oriental with a typical modern structure: lots of cassis with power-flowers tuberose, orange flower and gardenia and a base like a cashmere wrap. Sultry, a little airless.

Story

Contains an abundance of gardenia, known as 'the flower of spiritual ruin'. Organza was a favourite fabric of Hubert de Givenchy, though at the time of this perfume's launch he had bowed out, and John Galliano was designing. Givenchy is now designed by another Englishman – Alexander McQueen.

The bottle, is meant to be a stylized version of a Greek goddess. Organza Indécence (a follow-up scent) has the same goddess bottle but with her dress blowing open, flasher style.

Shocking

Character

Intensely sweet and flagrantly sensual. It *smells* pink. When this perfume was launched it was rumoured to have been based on the *oderata sexualis* of a woman. I think not, but it's heady stuff anyway.

Story

Elsa Schiaparelli, the surrealist fashion designer, wrote: 'The colour flashed in front of my eyes. Bright, impossible, impudent . . . a colour of China and Peru but not of the West – a shocking colour, pure and undiluted. So I called the perfume *Shocking!* The colour, used for the box, is known to this day as shocking pink. For the launch she called in Salvador Dali who dyed a huge teddy bear shocking pink and gave it a bellyful of drawers stuffed with bottles. The famous torso bottle, by Baccarat, based on Mae West's measurements, has been relaunched.

Top notes
Hyacinth, bergamot, narcissus, ylang-ylang
Middle notes
Rose, jasmine, syringa
Base notes
Sandalwood, labdanum, musk, honey

House	Schiaparelli
Date	1937
Perfumer	Jean Carles

Ysatis

Top notes
Mandarin, orange flower, ylang-ylang
Middle notes
Tuberose, jasmine, rose, orris
Base notes
Sandalwood, patchouli, amber, oakmoss, bay rum, clove, vanilla, musk, civet, castoreum

House	Givenchy
Date	1984
Perfumer	Dominique Ropion

Character

Languorous unfolding of rich flower oils, mainly tuberose, orange flower and ylang-ylang with bright mandarin at the introduction followed by a little powder in the heart. The base echoes with tantalizing animal notes and spices. *Haute bourgeois.*

Story

The name may sound like that of some Egyptian high priestess, but in fact it was made up by the president of Parfums Givenchy, Jean Courtiére. The *jus* is unusual in that it is balanced between several fragrance families: floral, oriental and chypre.

Boucheron

Character

Unlike many modern orientals and semi-orientals, this one is beautifully balanced. It unfolds magisterially from orange and apricot top notes with a background of cool green galbanum into a heart where flowers are interwoven with the deep-pile of vanilla, amber and civet. It dies away with the marmoreal purity of benzoin, sandalwood and olibanum. Queenly.

Story

Boucheron has a wonderful bottle shaped like a giant cabochon sapphire ring, a fitting offering from these grand Parisian jewellers whose company dates back to 1858. Sapphires have always been one of their specialities, like the diamond and sapphire necklace Frédéric Boucheron once made for the wealthy American Mrs Clarence Hickey, set with the largest sapphire ever known.

Perfume-jewels were popular in previous centuries when rings and necklaces often featured a jewel that twisted open to reveal a phial of scent or smelling salts and these were the inspiration for this bottle. In the nineteenth century Boucheron also made scent bottles into which rich women would decant their favourite fragrances; the usual practice at the time.

An interesting idea is their *les pluriels* bottle which is a twisted column, inspired by the one in the centre of the Place Vendôme in Paris, with two sprays, one for Boucheron eau de parfum, the other for their second fragrance, Jaïpur (see p. 122).

Top notes	
Bergamot, galbanum, mandarin, apricot, basil, marigold	
Middle notes	
Tuberose, narcissus, orange flower, jasmine, ylang-ylang, orris, broom	
Base notes	
Sandalwood, vanilla, tonka bean, amber, benzoin, olibanum, civet, musk	

House	Boucheron
Date	1988
Perfumer	Francis Deléamont and Jean-Pierre Béthouart

Narcisse Noir

Character

Smell this and suddenly you understand what it is about Catherine Deneuve. A sexy, warm skin-smell, yet gloriously *haute bourgeois*. Begins with a sudden epiphany of orangey citrus notes, quickly underscored with powdery, clean mid-notes, already complicated by rich, creamy base notes that last and last, coalescing on the skin. Narcotic. What the French call *troublant* – disturbing, in a good sense.

Top notes
Bergamot, lemon, mandarin, petitgrain
Middle notes
Orange flower, jasmine, rose, narcissus
Base notes
Musk, sandalwood, civet

House	Caron
Date	1912
Perfumer	Ernest Daltroff

Story

A phenomenon at the time of its launch, Narcisse Noir (black narcissus) was later worn by Gloria Swanson in *Sunset Boulevard*. It utilized new floral absolutes and synthetic aroma chemicals to create powerful new harmonies. And then there's the catcall of civet. If you want to walk in an ambiance of lounge pyjama languor, try this.

Tiffany

Character

Brings back the 80s as powerfully as a set of overstuffed shoulder pads. Cassis used at these concentrations was typical of that decade, especially on a dense amber and vanilla base. Feisty.

Top notes
Cassis, mandarin, plum, marigold, orange flower
Middle notes
Jasmine, damascene rose, lily of the valley, violet leaves, tuberose, ylang-ylang, heliotrope, orris
Base notes
sandalwood, amber, vanilla, tonka bean, vetiver

House	Tiffany
Date	1987
Perfumer	Jacques Polge

Story

Launched to celebrate 150 years of the jewellers Tiffany, the scent also contains 150 ingredients, one for every year. The bottle (Tiffany refer to it as the streamlined vessel) echoes the Art Deco design of their New York flagship store on Fifth Avenue. The flacon comes in a box tinted that strangely irresistible robin's egg blue.

Loulou

Character

An instant hit of bergamot gives way to the intense sweet fruit notes of cassis, plum and marigold. Rich floral heart with a hint of heliotrope.

Story

Arthur Gell wrote an essay called 'Perfume, Magic, Dream'. This could be the motto of Parfums Cacharel. Loulou, from the same stable as AnaïsAnaïs, is inspired by the character Lulu played by 1920s siren Louise Brooks in Pabst's silent film of 1928, *Pandora's Box*. The aim was to make something more seductive than AnaïsAnaïs, but with the naive seductiveness of a young woman. Dior's Poison was also an inspiration, both for the fragrance and the spirit of the bottle. Designed by Annegret Beier, it could be a small flacon of potent poison, mysterious and malignant.

Top notes	
Cassis, violet, plum, bergamot, marigold, mace, aniseed	
Middle notes	
Ylang-ylang, jasmine, heliotrope, tiara	
Base notes	
Tonka bean, cedar, vetiver, orris, musk	

House	Cacharel
Date	1987
Perfumer	Jean Guichard

Jaïpur

Character

Reflects the 1990s trend for foodie fragrances with the acid tang of pear drops and concentrated fruits followed by sweet flowers and strident base notes. Means business.

Story

Named for the city in India, the bottle is shaped like an Indian Nauratan bracelet, once given to young brides to ward off evil. Rajasthan legend tells that gems were formed from the fossilizing body of a demon struck down by the gods. His bones turned to diamonds, his teeth to pearls, his blood to rubies, his nails to chrysoberyl, his fat to crystal and coral, and his eyes to sapphires. The bracelets were studded with these stones. Jaïpur is also an echo of the scented, jewel-encrusted talismans carried by Europeans to ward off evils in previous centuries.

Top notes	
Plum flowers and fruit, peach, pineapple, freesia	
Middle notes	
Rose, acacia, orris, jasmine, heliotrope	
Base notes	
Amber, oakmoss, musk, vanilla, sandalwood, styrax	

House	Boucheron
Date	1988
Perfumer	Sophia Grojsman & Jean-Pierre Mary

Python

Character

Leftfield. Tingling medicine-cabinet high note, then for a glorious couple of minutes, smells identical to the pink Bazooka bubblegums you popped as a kid. Mid-note of red fruit and cool cardamom smells intriguing and fresh. Sensual but transparent oriental base with a hint of chocolate.

Story

Python, which comes in a python-printed box, sounds like the scent of a slinky seductress, but it isn't. From the Italian leather company enjoying a renaissance thanks to the quality and quiet good taste of their leather goods and clothes.

Top notes
Bergamot, mandarin
Middle notes
Plum, rose, jasmine,
nutmeg, cardamom
Base notes
Chocolate, sandalwood,
benzoin, vanilla

House	Trussardi
Date	1999
Perfumer	panel at
	Givaudan
	Roure

Cašmir

Top notes
Mango, coconut, peach,
cassis, raspberry
Middle notes
Rosewood, jasmine, man-
darin, cinnamon
Base notes
Amber, vanilla, tonka
bean, opopanax, musk

House	Chopard
Date	1991
Perfumer	Michel
	Almairac

Character

Nose candy. Smells rather like the parma violets great aunts used to suck to sweeten their breath. Raspberry sticks out, then yummy vanilla pudding.

Story

In the early 1990s came a wave of comfort scents centred on the urge to eat/scent our way out of recession. At the launch of Cašmir in New York journalists sat down to a lunch that featured many of Cašmir's ingredients. First they tucked into lobster in vanilla sauce, followed by quail with jasmine rice served with baked peaches, and finally, a dessert of iced mango with orange sauce and coconut ice-cream. 'At first I thought, I'd rather eat this stuff than smell of it,' said one journalist, 'but by the end I felt excited to have rediscovered the connection between food and sensuality.' The name refers to the Indian state of Kashmir.

Poison

Character

Aggressively fruity, spicy and, above all, musky. It may look like a fruit, but it acts like an olfactory hand grenade.

Story

In a world of 'me-too' fragrances all smelling of pretty flowers, thank God for this little vial of venom. Never mind what it smells like, everything about it has personality. This Dior fragrance picked up the poisoned chalice of Opium, and took it forward. 'Both Poison and Opium are feminist fragrances in different ways', says psychologist Joachim Mensing. 'Opium symbolizes woman's emancipation through her inner search. Poison is about power in sexual politics. It looks like a magic fruit filled with belladonna. It promises the power of witchcraft. It's the female fantasy of sexual domination. He will be passive under your spell, subject to your will.' Indeed, how could he not be with his entire ear, nose and throat system anaesthetized by the fumes of your fragrance?

Scent has always been sold as bottled sex, but it has to be forbidden sex to be truly alluring. 'The impulse towards transgression is very bound up with why we buy fragrance', says Mensing. 'Life is all about routine. Wearing a "sinful" scent is a way of living out your alter ego's ideal existence without the risks of acting it out in real life.' Poison – the best name for a perfume since Chanel No5 – comes from an illustrious line. My Sin, by Lanvin (1925), Miss Jezebel (1938), Deviltry (1936), Spanking by Schiaparelli, and Suivez-moi Jeune Homme ('Follow Me Young Man', 1926) were not Mother's Day fragrances.

Poison was the brainchild of Dior's Maurice Roger, and marked a stark departure from the company's ladylike style. The original bottle, designed by glass-blower Véronique Monod, was a purple apple with malignant vapours snaking up it. It had to be an apple: think of Eve and of the Wicked Queen from Snow White. In our culture, the poisoned apple is the purveyor of sex and death.

Top notes	
Orange flower, honey, berries, pimento	
Middle notes	
Cinnamon, coriander, pepper, mace, plum, anise, tuberose, ylang-ylang	
Base notes	
Ambergris, ladanum, opopanax	

House	Christian Dior
Date	1985
Perfumer	Edouard Flechier

Dolce & Gabbana

Character

Flowers on drugs. First there's the bite of citrus, then a vortex of blossom. Having flailed through this, you only have strength left to suspire on the red velvet pillows of musk and amber. Va-va-voom.

Story

This olfactory equivalent of a Wonderbra comes from Italian designers Domenico Dolce and Stefano Gabbana. They are famed for their flagrantly sensual designs that celebrate the female form, and often take inspiration from the Cinecittà. They have also done collections based round the garb of Sicilian widows. Their press office says this is a scent beloved by Cindy Crawford, Madonna, Cher and Martine McCutcheon. We should have known.

Top notes
Petitgrain, bitter orange, tangerine, lemon, basil, ivy, aldehydes, freesia
Middle notes
Lily of the valley, tuberose, jasmine, neroli, rose, carnation, marigold, coriander, heliotrope, orris
Base notes
Sandalwood, musk, vanilla, amber, tonka bean

House	Dolce & Gabbana
Date	1992
Perfumer	panel at IFF

Sonia Rykiel

Top notes
Cassis, passionfruit, pineapple, mandarin, cardamom
Middle notes
Honeysuckle, rose, lily of the valley, violet
Base notes
Vanilla, cinnamon, caramel, tonka bean, amber, musk, cedar

House	Sonia Rykiel
Date	1998
Perfumer	Jean-Louis Sieuzac

Character

Rykiel says the *jus* is all about seduction, the equivalent of a 'results dress'. And certainly, a starving man might be driven to bite into a woman wearing this as though she were a hot fruit pie. Sieuzac, who also created Opium and Dune, gives the fruits more punch than most, then slathers them in caramel and vanilla. Humorous.

Story

Sonia Rykiel is a veteran Parisian designer who specializes in slinky knitwear. The bottle is shaped like a short-sleeved sweater, either in solid gold or with a ritzy diamante logo across the 'chest'. As the press release memorably puts it: 'The sensuous double game of a sweater and a perfume.'

Theorema

Character

Terry's Chocolate Orange as a perfume. First, out rolls the fat, happy smell of chocolate and oranges – provided by tangelos and Thai shamouti. Soon odalisque spiciness segues in, turning it from corner-shop confectionery to Sultanic snack. Dries down to a base of warm milk and animal notes with rosy guaîacwood: a newly popular accord first seen in Le Feu d'Issey (see p. 128). Sticky.

Story

There is a certain kind of scent the French call *le parfum fourrure*. It is rich, voluptuous, warming in winter and enhanced by the catty odour of a fur coat. This fragrance from the Fendi sisters, famous for their fur designs, fits the bill. Everything about the gold and black packaging too bespeaks that peculiarly Italian type of in-your-face luxury.

FENDI

THEOREMA

Top notes	
Tangelos, shamouti, eglantine	
Middle notes	
Jasmine, cinnamon, pink pepper, osmanthus	
Base notes	
Musk, macassar, milky note, amber, guaîacwood, sandalwood	

House	Fendi
Date	1998
Perfumer	Christina Nagel

Ghost

Top notes	
Ambrette seed, rose	
Middle notes	
Jasmine, hibiscus, apricot	
Base notes	
Incense, sandalwood, vanilla, musk, amber	

House	Ghost
Date	1999
Perfumer	Michel Almairac

Character

Avalanche of sweet white flowers accented with the warm peachiness of ambrette seeds. As these fade, a slightly peppery, mellow warmth builds till your skin smells as though basted with caramel and apricot jam. A light oriental from the current star performer who also created Gucci's Rush (see p. 128).

Story

Ghost, designed by Tanya Sarne, is a British fashion house known for its feminine, floaty clothes often in trademark crinkly viscose. Sarne wanted the scent to be 'understated in a feminine way, like the clothes'. She was inspired by Femme, the scent her mother wore, but wanted 'a modern, romantic interpretation of those old-fashioned fragrances, something ethereal, light and fresh'. The curvy bottle was inspired by a glass vase by Vennini, a famous glassblower from the turn of the century.

Angel

Character

A love-hate perfume and a thoroughly modern one. Back in the 1920s, for example, no-one, not even a woman with the all-too-appropriate name of Coco Chanel, would have thought a perfume that smelt of chocolate good for anything but a bedtime drink. Chocolate has been shown chemically to induce feelings similar to the bliss of falling in love. And Dr Susan Schiffman, Professor of Medical Psychology at Duke University, has experimented with chocolate as a means of treating depression.

Mugler said he wanted a perfume that smelled of the funfairs of his childhood, of candyfloss, toffee apples and chocolate bars. Olivier Cresp, the perfumer, added another inspired funfair note, patchouli, which reminded him of the bittersweet smell of sawdust. Angel is also very fruity in the top notes. It's the most extreme, but also one of the most successful, of the gourmand fragrances of the 1990s. As Jane Withering writes in her poem *Wicked Chocolate*, 'Twill make old women young and fresh, create new motions of the flesh'.

Top notes
Bergamot, hedione, helional
Middle notes
Dewberry, honey
Base notes
Patchouli, chocolate, caramel, vanilla, coumarin

House	Thierry Mugler
Date	1992
Perfumer	Olivier Cresp & Yves de Chiris

Story

Thierry Mugler is known for his spectacular catwalk shows and warrior-women clothes. My favourite of his catwalk creations were women dressed as human motorbikes. Hell's angels and heavens too, are the symbols for Angel, the scent. Mugler designed the star bottle himself. Perfumes are often like designers little fetishes: Chanel chose her lucky number for No5; Dior chose his lucky flower, lily of the valley, as the note for Diorissimo; Mugler chose the star, his lucky symbol, for the Angel bottle. He also wears the star symbol as a tattoo and as a ring.

Le Feu d'Issey

Character

Combines the transparency of an aqueous note with the fieriness of spice.

All wrapped up in an almost tactile milky, vanilla-like note, warmed with a drop of amber. Guaîacwood has a gentle rosy scent and is sometimes used to adulterate rose oil. Opalescent. A subtle come hither.

Story

Le Feu d'Issey ('the fire of Issey') follows on from the highly successful L'Eau d'Issey ('the water of Issey'). 'Issey wanted a ball of fire,' says Catherine Hellegouarch, marketing director. 'So it's a perfect sphere, lit up from inside by a "twisted" flame'. The beauty of the bottle becomes apparent when you turn it in your hand and the flame flickers.

Top notes	
Damascene rose, coriander leaves	
Middle notes	
Pepper, golden Japanese lily	
Base notes	
Guaîacwood, milk notes, amber, benzoin	

House	Issey Miyake
Date	1998
Perfumer	Jacques Cavalier

Rush

Top notes	
Freesia	
Middle notes	
Gardenia, jasmine, damascene rose, coriander	
Base notes	
Vanilla headspace, patchouli, vetiver	

House	Gucci
Date	1999
Perfumer	Michel Almairac

Character

Milk-soft, gently spicy and a little reminiscent of Le Feu d'Issey. It's a skin-scent, with a low-key, sexy drydown like saffron simmered in milk.

Story

Utterly original and the ultimate in metropolitan chic, the 'bottle' for Rush looks like a red plastic video cassette. It comes in a metallic red sleeve lined in scarlet suede. That hidden suede says everything about this scent. Tom Ford, Gucci designer at the time, wanted the scent to evoke 'the idea of when you meet somebody and you don't know what it is. There's just this . . . little electric sort of rush'.

Tabu

Character

Cat on a hot tin roof, mewling in heat. Tabu is weird, wonderfully weird, and shockingly sexual. It rolls open with a beautiful orange flower accord, but already you're being knocked sideways and pulled in two different directions. One direction is Tabu's famous patchouli-carnation accord. Patchouli, used at a huge concentration of ten per cent, gives a dark, disturbing mystery. The carnation is all powdery, clovey heat. And the other direction? Civet, that catcall to carnality. Tabu has oodles of it; suave, full of volume, and scorchingly sexy. For women who wear their knickers on their heads.

Story

Javier Serra launched his Spanish perfume house, Dana, with this perfume. The name, Tabu ('taboo') came to him when his eye fell on a copy of Freud's *Totem and Taboo*. Fitting. Apparently he asked for '*un parfum de puta*' or a whore's brew.

Top notes
Bergamot, orange flower, basil, neroli, coriander
Middle notes
Carnation, jasmine, rose, clover, ylang-ylang
Base notes
Patchouli, civet, oakmoss, amber, musk, vetiver, sandalwood, cedar, benzoin, vanilla

House	Dana
Date	1932
Perfumer	Jean Carles

Boudoir

Top notes
Bergamot, mandarin, viburnum headspace
Middle notes
Tobacco flower, cardamon, coriander, orris, rose, cinnamon
Base notes
Amber, vanilla, sandalwood

House	Vivienne Westwood
Date	1998
Perfumer	Martin Gras

Character

Smooth, sweet bouquet spiked withpepper and spices. Accent of viburnum, a shrub whose headspace is copied for the first time here. Warm, vibrating amber base. Blooms on the skin.

Story

The first scent from the great British designer, Vivienne Westwood, who, with then husband Malcolm McLaren, launched the punk look on a reeling world and now creates clothes that draw on centuries-old tailoring traditions. 'I wanted this perfume to smell of our sexual smells,' she says, 'or at least to have that warm-skin smell. But I also wanted it to be intellectual. I want my fragrance to give a woman presence. What attracted me to the idea of a "boudoir" is that it's a private space like a capsule.'

Opium

Character

Opium has an illustrious ancestry. You can trace its development back through great classics such as Tabu, Youth-Dew and Shalimar (see pp. 129, 132, and 139); yet it also stands alone. Its baroque top note yokes together plummy, spicy nuances with crisp bergamot and lemon. The heart is all smoky, peppery spice and somnolent balsams. Only then comes the sweet roundness of the flower oils. The base is quite woody but with an animal darkness. To be worn lying down.

Story

If it hadn't been for Yves Saint Laurent's obstreperous genius, we would never have had a perfume with such a fabulous name. Squibb, the American parent company of Parfums Saint Laurent at the time, felt the name endorsed drug use. They wanted to call it Black Orchid. Flacon-designer Dinand's autobiography tells us: 'He wanted a bottle that would evoke the orient. I had been working on the stylization of an object that the Japanese samurai hung on their belts. It was a small wooden box containing several drawers which were held together by strings that passed through each side. Generally there was a small sculpted ball on the top. This box is called an inro and the ball a netsuke. The samurai wore these boxes, and in the different drawers kept spices, medicinal herbs, salt and opium for soothing the pain of wounds.' Saint Laurent recognized the design immediately. 'That's it,' he said. 'This will be the greatest perfume in the world and we'll call it Opium.' Squibb's fears were not unfounded. The American Coalition Against Opium and Drug Use and the Federal Justice Department tried to have Opium outlawed. In other countries it had to be imported under a pseudonym because of drug import laws and relabelled inside the country. But this only fuelled the craze for the forbidden perfume. The launch party was the first of the mega-launches, held on a junk in Manhattan's East River. The column inches it and the name created, as well as the heavy sillage of the smell, ensured Opium a massive success.

Top notes	
Aldehydes, plum, pepper, tangerine, coriander, bergamot, lemon	
Middle notes	
Clove, jasmine, cinnamon, rose, peach, orris, myrrh, ylang-ylang	
Base notes	
Benzoin, patchouli, opopanax, cedar, sandalwood, labdanum, castoreum, musk, vanilla	

House	Yves Saint Laurent
Date	1997
Perfumer	Jean-Louis Sieuzac

Hypnotic Poison

Character

Bitter, like some thrilling new cough medicine. If Snow White's poisoned apple had tasted like this she would have spat it out immediately. The harsh, demonic note continues to sound while sambac jasmine, a close, heavy bloom, entwines with vanilla and musk to imprison the wearer in a throbbing mesh. Trippy.

Story

Aimed at the modern temptress, Hypnotic Poison was inspired by Poison, Dior's famous scent of 1985. Poison originally had a purple apple-shaped bottle, retained in crimson for Hypnotic. The glass is dipped in liquid vinyl giving it a fetishy rubber feel. John Galliano became Dior's designer in 1996 and he designed a special bottle for the pure parfum, the Diable Rouge (red devil) with garnet beads round the neck.

Coco

Character

A cascade of sizzling spices gives Coco a sultry crackle from its overture. This then snakes skilfully through sweet, sharply delineated flowers in the mid-notes. Cool, enigmatic resins contrast with ambery and vanilla warmth in the base. Haughty but flushed.

Story

When Chanel was formulating No19, she toyed with the idea of calling it Coco. At the time, there was a musical of her life, called *Coco*, starring Katharine Hepburn. But it was not a name she liked much. Gabrielle was her real name, Coco a nickname her father had given her. The scent was inspired by perfumer Jacques Polge's visit to Chanel's apartment on the rue Cambon, a series of casketlike rooms decorated with Venetian glass, leather books and oriental screens. Polge says he wanted to capture this baroque side of Chanel in a perfume.

Youth Dew

Character

The personality of a 1950s housewife: super-efficient, always with a roast in the oven, but in full make-up and stilettos. Springs open with frosty aldehydes, then a comforting, uncompromising spiciness dominated by clove with warm cinnamon. The base is startling: medicinal, starched balsams, which, like a nurse's uniform, are perversely sexy.

Story

Dolores del Rio pronounced that the secret of 'driving men ga-ga' was to brush your hair with this fragrance then sweep it all up on top of your head. A shrewd marketer, Mrs Lauder launched it as a perfumed bath oil at a time when women were no more likely to buy perfume for themselves than they would a dozen red roses. It worked. A veteran.

Top notes	
Orange, bergamot, aldehydes	
Middle notes	
Clove, carnation, rose, ylang-ylang, cinnamon, acacia, jasmine	
Base notes	
Amber, tolu balsam, olibanum, oakmoss, Peru balsam, vanilla, patchouli	

House	Estée Lauder
Date	1953
Perfumer	unknown

Feminité du Bois

Character

A fantastic and unusual perfume, though not for everyone. Baudelaire wrote that some perfumes 'sing the transports of the spirit and the senses' and cedar is like that; both austere and sensual. This sombre perfume is dominated by cedar and spices: cinnamon and cardamom especially. Opulent, what you imagine Cleopatra might have worn.

Story

'Feminity of the Wood' is the brainchild of Serge Lutens who designs all the fragrances for Shiseido. It grew from his love of Morocco, especially the cedar forests of the Atlas mountains. But, he says, 'my aim is not to create a perfume with cedar but to capture the emotion of this wood'.

Top notes	
Peach, rosewood, tarragon	
Middle notes	
Cinnamon, damascene rose, honey, beeswax, mace, violet, orange flower	
Base notes	
Cedarwood, cardamom, clove, sandalwood, amber, musk, patchouli, civet	

House	Shiseido
Date	1992
Perfumer	Pierre Bourdon & Christopher Sheldrake

Coup de Fouet

Character

Outrageous aroma of black pepper soon harmonizes audaciously with unbelievably strong clove carnation. Will keep you as warm as a fur coat in winter. It's what Cruella de Vil would have worn. Wear it when you're feeling similarly vicious.

Story

A brilliant name. Coup de Fouet is French for 'crack of the whip'. It is the eau de toilette version of another Caron scent, Poivre (pepper), and, like Poivre, comes in a bottle studded with 'peppercorns'. The great, but little-known, French house of Caron is covered further in Fleur de Rocaille Classique (see p. 58).

Top notes	
Red pepper, clove, pepper	
Middle notes	
Carnation, ylang-ylang	
Base notes	
Opopanax, vetiver, sandalwood, oakmoss	

House	Caron
Date	1954
Perfumer	unknown

Comme des Garçons

Top notes	
Galbanum, cardamom, clove, black pepper	
Middle notes	
Rose, geranium	
Base notes	
Cedar, styrax, labdanum, honey, benzoin	

House	Comme des Garçons
Date	1994
Perfumer	Mark Buxton & panel at Haarmann & Reimer

Character

Hot, spicy, strong and linear. A bravely uncommercial smell that one journalist compared to curry. Kawakubo said she wanted it to 'work like Ayurvedic medicine and behave like a drug'. And it does. Luckily, its mule's kick is aimed at your olfactory bulb, not your adrenals.

Story

Rei Kawakubo, the Japanese woman behind the Comme des Garçons label, is, like Issey Miyake, a designer who pushes fashion's envelope with her intellectually challenging clothes. She created the famous black 'bag-lady' look of the early 80s that arty types favoured over power suits. She shares something else with Miyake: she doesn't much like scent, and doesn't wear it. Comes in an off-kilter bottle stamped with a barcode, and shrink-wrapped in a big squidgy sheet of plastic.

Black

Character

Wonderfully original, resolutely modern scent with a smoky top note of lapsang souchong tea leaves. That would make it different enough, but in the mid-notes hot rubber tyres are clearly detectable, allied to cool, cerebral resinous notes. Many modern fragrances claim interesting new accords, few deliver like this one. A turn-on in a 'sex in the head' kind of way.

Top notes	
Lapsang tea, smoke accord	
Middle notes	
Resin accord, rubber accord	
Base notes	
Amber, woody accord	

House	Bulgari
Date	1998
Perfumer	Annick Menaigo

Story

Italian jewellers Bulgari continue their tea theme with Black, stylishly packaged in a black rubber ring. They bravely say it's not for everybody – good news, not another 'me too' scent designed to be commercial.

Dune

Top notes
Bergamot, mandarin, wallflower, aldehydes, rosewood, green note
Middle notes
Broom, rose, peony, lily, jasmine, orris
Base notes
Lichen, amber, musk, patchouli, benzoin, sandalwood

House	Christian Dior
Date	1991
Perfumer	Jean-Louis Sieuzac

Character

Extraordinary olfactive landscape created by the quite harsh, pungent, bracken-and-honey feel of broom with the tarriness of lichen, against a warm amber and musk base.

Story

Dior wanted to do a marine type fragrance, but without the ozonic notes. The launch, at the chic resort of Biarritz, was a huge media extravaganza with practically the whole town painted in Dune's peach livery and a smart picnic on the beach. But someone had forgotten to alert Dior that it was a nudist beach . . .

Samsara

Character

A scent with a stonking big beat. You can easily miss the fruity top note as the carnal roar of jasmine and sandalwood in heat tear through your olfactory nerve. The heavy bass comes from a megadose of Mysore sandalwood blended with a new synthetic sandalwood. Its marriage with jasmine is hot-tempered and passionate. The sandalwood note lingers . . . and lingers.

Story

Launched exactly one hundred years after Jicky, it was created as a talisman to give Guerlain commercial success into the next century. Samsara is a Sanskrit word meaning 'eternal return'. Not a happy concept for Buddhists who want to escape samsara for Nirvana. But a very happy concept for the Guerlain sales force.

Top notes
Bergamot, lemon, peach, tarragon
Middle notes
Jasmine, rose, orris, ylang-ylang, carnation
Base notes
Sandalwood, vanilla, amber, musk, tonka bean

House	Guerlain
Date	1989
Perfumer	Jean-Paul Guerlain

Bal à Versailles

Top notes
Bergamot, lemon, mandarin, neroli
Middle notes
Jasmine, rose de mai, lily of the valley, ylang-ylang, orris, musk, civet, ambergris
Base notes
Cedar, sandalwood, benzoin, tolu balsam, sweet clover

House	Jean Desprez
Date	1962
Perfumer	Jean Desprez

Character

Follows the classic development of a grand French perfume of an earlier age: citrus top notes melting into a melodious accord of natural flowers with dense, velvety orris and sensuous animal notes. The surprise: a monastic drydown of resins and woods.

Story

Unusually for the latter part of this century, Bal à Versailles ('ball at Versailles') was launched directly by its perfumer, Jean Desprez. Desprez was the great-grandson of F. Millot who created the great classic Crêpe de Chine for the house of Millot in 1925. He married hatmaker Lily Daché who launched two perfumes of her own in surrealist bottles, Dashing and Drifting. The back of the label shows a reproduction of a Fragonard painting.

Eau
de
Toilette
Bal à Versailles
Jean Desprez
PARIS

Vol de Nuit

Top notes	
Orange, bergamot, lemon, mandarin	

Middle notes	
Galbanum, violet, rosewood, palmarosa, jasmine, pimento	

Base notes	
Vanilla, benzoin, balsam of Peru, musk, leather, orris, sandalwood	

House	Guerlain
Date	1933
Perfumer	Jacques Guerlain

Character

A burst of orange then cool wood and balsam notes wrapping the flowers in sophistication. A hint of hot spice. Leathery and enigmatic.

Story

Nowadays, the idea of a fragrance dedicated to an airline is about as romantic as one dedicated to a bus route. But back in 1933, when Air France was born, the idea of flight was as thrilling as space travel. The name, meaning night flight, was taken from the eponymous novel *Vol de Nuit* by Antoine de Saint-Exupéry (who also wrote *Le Petit Prince*). Saint-Exupéry was an aviator. His plane disappeared in 1944 during a mission above occupied France and his body was never recovered. Now, every year, the French Air Force College orders bottles of Vol de Nuit emblazoned with the French Air Force emblem for its cadets to give out on official visits abroad.

Tiempe Passate

Top notes	
Bergamot, clementine, sage, peach	

Middle notes	
Montauk rose, mimosa, cyclamen	

Base notes	
White orris, cedar, ambrette seeds, musk	

House	Antonio Ballanca-Mahoney
Date	1999
Perfumer	Norbert Bijaoui

Character

The moment where the citrus and sage top note falls away in an unctuous wave of orris is exquisite. Orris, the rhizome of the iris and one of the most expensive ingredients in perfumery, smells like a hybrid of flesh and flower. But it's so expensive, you rarely find it in such quantity. Here, it is kept fluent and fresh by salty Montauk rose, androgynous cedar and the citrus notes.

Story

'I wanted a fragrance that melted into your skin; that didn't jump out at you,' explains Antonia Ballenca-Mahoney. 'I wanted it to be the way you feel after a night out drinking, dancing and dining. Next morning, you turn over on the pillow and your fragrance on your hair smells even better than it did the night before.' Means 'time passes' in Sicilian.

Moschino

Character

A double dose of bergamot and lemon gives a bright feel to the top note of freesia and honeysuckle with a hint of plum. The heart note is lush flowers counterpointed with spice and wood. The base is all heaving bosom. Adult.

Story

Franco Moschino was an Italian designer who made a hit in the 1980s by poking fun at the decade's status-driven vulgarity. He sent jackets down the runway with the price or the word 'couture' embroidered cheekily across the back. He died in 1994, but his fashion house continues.

PARFUM
MOSCHINO

Top notes
Bergamot, lemon, galbanum, marigold, rosewood, freesia, honeysuckle, plum
Middle notes
Rose, ylang-ylang, gardenia, carnation, nutmeg, pepper, sandalwood
Base notes
Amber, musk, vanilla

House	Moschino
Date	1987
Perfumer	Firmenich

Magie Noire

Character

A true oriental, dense and caressing as a fur coat, thick with the hypnotic odour of full-blown, dark red roses. It dies away to amber and incense with a whiff of burnt sugar.

Story

Lancôme have a penchant for re-using names of their old scents. Trésor was first used in 1952, and Magie in 1949. Magie Noire (black magic) followed Opium into the territory of the forbidden and the occult. The bottle, designed by Pierre Dinand, was inspired by the medieval alembics used in alchemy and the original box was covered in cabbalistic signs symbolizing bismuth, verdigris, sulphur and gold. Just before the launch, they took the precaution of omitting symbols that could be considered maleficent.

Top notes
Galbanum, bergamot, blackcurrant buds, hyacinth
Middle notes
Damascene rose, jasmine, tuberose, orris, honey, ylang-ylang
Base notes
Sandalwood, patchouli, labdanum, amber, civet, incense, civet, oakmoss, musk, castoreum

House	Lancôme
Date	1978
Perfumer	Gérard Coupy

MAGIE
NOIRE
LANCÔME
PARIS

Obsession

Character

Ann Gottlieb, who art directed the scent, briefed the perfumer to do 'sensuality with a touch of raunch' and 'classy with a touch of trash.' She got it, but with the emphasis reversed.

Top notes
Mandarin, bergamot
Middle notes
Jasmine, orange flower, ylang-ylang
Base notes
Vanilla, amber, civet, sandalwood, vetiver, musk, oakmoss, frankincense

House	Calvin Klein
Date	1985
Perfumer	Jean Guichard

Story

Together with Giorgio and Dior's Poison(see pp. 58 and 124), this fragrance will forever conjure up the 1980s, a decade associated with consumption, both material and carnal. Obsession played more on the carnal aspect with one famous advertisement involving a dimly lit tangle of naked bodies and another with a nude couple on a swing. The imagery capitalized on Klein's reputation as a sexual provocateur, established in the 1970s with his jeans campaign and with Brooke Shields (What comes between me and my Calvins? Nothing.)

Ambre Sultan

Top notes
Oregano, bay leaf, coriander, myrtle,
Middle notes
Angelica, patchouli,
Base notes
Labdanum, styrax, Tolu balsam, benzoin, sandalwood

House	Serge Lutens
Date	April 2000
Perfumer	Christopher Sheldrake

Character

Every so often a scent is launched which is supposed to smell of the *odorata sexualis* of a woman. This actually does. Remarkably – to some, repugnantly – it reeks of a woman's sexual juices. It's based on the lumps of vegetal amber found in Moroccan souks. 'An amalgam of resins, flowers and spices, these Moroccan ambers are monuments in praise of woman's skin,' says Lutens.

Story

At the Salons du Palais-Royal, an olfactory seraglio has been created by Serge Lutens, for years the creative force at Shiseido. The perfumes sold here are rare and enigmatic, often spicy or rich in resins. You'll find a scent that exudes pure myrrh, another based on absinthe. Now a handful of these scents are available at selected department stores worldwide.

Shalimar

Character

'Bizarre deity, brown as the night/Your perfume mingles musk and havana' wrote Baudelaire. He would have liked Shalimar, the most oriental of perfumes. It smells like an Arab sheik, bronze in timbre, resonating with warmth, and reeking of sensuality. It opens quite violently with a flood of lemony-orange bergamot, softened with a little woody note. But it's full of movement at this stage: already the patchouli and vetiver of the mid-note are complimenting the citrus, making a bridge to the suave, spicy balsams – it's this which gives the bronzy feeling. Now comes the fragrance's real beauty – the orchestration of its base notes. Almost prickly, spicy, balsamic – and animal. The creamy vanilla endures for hours.

Top notes
Bergamot, lemon, mandarin, rosewood
Middle notes
Patchouli, rose, jasmine, orris, vetiver, heliotrope
Base notes
Opopanax, vanilla, civet, benzoin, Peru balsam, tonka bean, sandalwood

House	Guerlain
Date	1925
Perfumer	Jacques Guerlain

Story

When a new synthetic vanilla, ethyl vanillin, was delivered to his laboratory, Jacques Guerlain picked it up and absent-mindedly poured a large dose into a bottle of Jicky just to see what would happen. The result was the basic accord of Shalimar, a perfume which pushed the oriental element in Jicky to new extremes. Shalimar's phenomenal success did not come overnight. Created in 1921, it had to wait till 1925 to be launched and, at first, found more success in America where its potency was appreciated.

The name was taken from the Gardens of Shalimar, which the Mughal Emperor Shah Jahan had laid out in 1619. The word means 'the abode of love' and Shah Jahan walked in the gardens with the wife he adored, Mumtaz Mahal. She died in childbirth three years after he succeeded his father to the throne, and he built the Taj Mahal as her monument.

Must de Cartier

Character

An insolent green note opens then echoes through slowly evolving siren notes of civet and amber with a touch of narcissus. The theme is continued on a more profound key by benzoin and sandalwood, played against warm vanilla. Poised. Sublime.

Story

Cartier was founded in 1847. It was Louis, grandson of the founder, who gained 15 royal warrants to the courts of Europe. Cartier had always designed scent bottles for rich clients, but in 1938 they began to plan a series of scents named for famous stones: Koh-i-Noor, Nassak and Cumberland. The war put paid to this plan. Les Musts de Cartier, the company's boutique line, featured a bestselling 1970's lighter and provided inspiration for their first bottle.

Top notes
Galbanum, neroli, mandarin, rosewood
Middle notes
Rose, narcissus, hedione (from jasmine)
Base notes
Civet, amber, opopanax, sandalwood, benzoin, musk, vanilla

House	Cartier
Date	1981
Perfumer	Jean-Jacques Diener

Habanita

Top notes
Bergamot, peach, orange flower
Middle notes
Oakmoss, jasmine de Grasse, patchouli
Base notes
Ambergris, leather, vetiver, benzoin, vanilla

House	Molinard
Date	1921
Perfumer	panel at Molinard and Roure

Character

Corrupt, sweet flesh of a sinner. This forgotten masterpiece makes many orientals of recent years seem like vulgar upstarts. With Habanita, you are borne along on the dusky, rolling wave of the ambergris note, allied to murky vetiver and patchouli and the odour of old leatherbound books. The fruit notes are lightly played, never sharp, the flowers hushed in the midst of all this plush. Like silk underwear under a fur coat. For latter-day *grandes horizontales*.

Story

In 1849, Molinard opened in Grasse in the south of France, once the centre of the perfume industry. The company still maintains a perfume distillery in the town, together with a charming Perfume Museum. The flacon for Habanita is an original René Lalique design, known as 'Beauty' and first used for Molinard's Les Isles d'Or. The *jus* was rejigged in 1988. Habanita means young woman from Havana.

Stockists and mail order numbers

Contacts for stockists and mail order for hard-to-find scents are listed below. Good sources in the UK generally are **Harrods** (020 7730 1234), **Harvey Nichols** (020 7235 5000), **Selfridges** (020 7629 1234), **Liberty** (020 7734 1234) **Beauty Base** for old designer scents (020 7229 5600 or 020 8572 1206) and **Les Senteurs** for small perfume houses (020 7328 1036, or mail order: 020 7730 2322) or on the Internet at **www.perfuma.com**

Acqua di Parma at Harvey Nichols (see above), Liberty (see above) and Fortnum & Mason: 020 7734 8040, mail order 0845 700 1707

Antonia's Flowers and **Tiempe Passate** for stockists: Space NK 020 7299 4999, also from Liberty (see above)

Attar for stockists: 01932 254854

Bal à Versailles, Ivoire, Jolie Madame, Ombre Rose, Sonia Rykiel and **Vent Vert**: Jean Patou at Harrods (see above, ext: 3020)

Bandit, Diesel Plus Plus Feminine, Fendi, Fracas, Indiscret and **Tiffany** for stockists: 0345 697072

Bijan Light from Beauty Base see above

Cabochard for stockists: 020 8398 5300

Chanel the rarer scents **Bois des Isles** and **Cuir de Russe** only from Chanel boutiques, mail order: 26 Old Bond Street, W1X 3DA, tel: 020 7493 5040

Citrus Paradisi for stockists and mail order: 0800 919728

Coup de Fouet, Fleurs de Rocaille Classique and **Narcisse Noir** from Harrods (see above)

Comme des Garcons and **Odeur 53** for stockists: 01372 275 932

Coriandre from Beauty Base (see above)

Neroli Sauvage and Fleurs de Bulgarie for mail order: Les Senteurs (see above)

L'Ombre dans L'Eau and **Philosykos** from Harrods, Liberty and Les Senteurs (see above); also from Lloyd Davis: Ridgefield House, 14 John Dalton Street, Manchester M2 6JR, tel: 0161 832 3700

Dirt from Harvey Nichols or order via the Internet at www.sephora.com or www.fashion-planet.com

Dali from Selfridges (see above, ext. 2821)

Diva for stockists: 020 8398 9717

Eau de Charlotte, Eau d'Hadrien and **Eau de Lavande** from Les Senteurs and Harrods (see above)

Eau d'Eté for mail order: 020 7761 0362, also from Harrods (see above)

Etiquette Bleue from Les Senteurs (see above)

Fidji from Harrods (see above) and Selfridges (see above, ext. 2922)

French Lime Blossom for mail order: 020 7720 0202 or visit www.jomalone.co.uk (for information only)

Ghost for stockists: 020 7499 4420

Habanita from Harrods (see above)

Halston from Beauty Base (see above)

Heliotrope from Jean Patou at Harvey Nichols (see above, ext. 2347)

Iceberg from Iceberg: 10 Sloane Street SW1, tel: 020 7259 6657, and from Harrods (see above) – both do mail order

Lalique for stockists: 020 7499 8228 or 020 7245 9090

La Perla for stockists: 020 7436 5864

Lily of the Valley for mail order: 0800 716108, for international mail order: +44 208 880 2050; fax: +44 207 619 6613 or e-mail: penhaligons@warnaco.com

Je Reviens for stockists: 01494 712 855

Ma Griffe from Jenners of Edinburgh: 0131 225 2442, and on the Internet at www.perfuma.com

Montana for stockists and mail order: 0345 697072

Mure et Musc and **Mimosa pour Moi** for stockists and mail order: 020 7352 4196

Must de Cartier for stockists: 020 7408 5700

Niki de St Phalle for stockists: 020 7580 6900; also from Harrods 020 7730 1234

Route de Thé exclusive to Barneys New York, tel: +1 212 826 8900

Secrete Datura is exclusive to Les Senteurs: 71 Elizabeth Street, London SW1W 9PJ, tel: 020 7730 2322)

Shocking from Harrods (see above)

Smell This buy over the Internet at www.smellthis.com

So de la Renta from Harvey Nichols and Selfridges (see above)

Special No. 127 for stockists and mail order: 0845 702 3239 or visit www.florislondon.com

Tabu from Beauty Base (see above)

Tiare from all branches of Space NK: 020 7299 4999, or for mail order: 0870 169 9999

Index

5th Avenue 67
24, Faubourg 43
212, 89
'1000', 45
4711, 97
accord 16, 18
Acqua di Giò 74
Acqua di Parma 92
aldehydes 12, 18, 46—52
All About Eve 74
allergic reaction 11
Allure 37
Almairac, Michel 66, 122, 126, 128
Alméras, Henri 42, 56
Amarige 64
amber 18, 136—9
Ambre Sultan 138
AnaïsAnaïs 28
Angel 127
animal odours 8, 15, 112—13, 140
Antonia's Flowers 31
Apel, David 76
Après L'Ondée 25
aqueous scents 12, 32—7, 73—81, 88—9
Arden, Elizabeth 26, 67, 76
Armani, Emporio 98
Armani, Giorgio 74, 83
Aromatics Elixir 103
Arpège 49
Arpels, Jacques 41
Astori, Alain 41
Attar 55
Aveda 96

Baby Doll 84
Bal à Versailles 135
Balmain, Pierre 22, 44, 113
Banaim, Carlos 63
Bandit 114
Barney's, New York 89
Baron, Fabien 75, 89, 96
base notes 10, 16, 18
bath oil 11, 132
Beauté de Chantecaille 55
Beautiful 61
Beaux, Ernest 47, 48, 50, 115
Becker, Calice 57

Beier, Annegret 122
Bell, Jimmy 67
Bellanca-Mahoney, Antonia 31, 136
Berard, James 90
Bergé, Pierre 109
Béthouart, Jean-Pierre 120
Bienaimé, Robert 53
Bijan, House of 65
Bijan Light 65
Bijaoui, Norbert 136
Birmane 67
Black 134
Blanchet, Maurice 52
Blonde 63
Blue Grass 26
Bobbi 88
Bocris, Francis 112
Bodenham, James 72
body odours 7, 8, 9
Bois des Iles 50
Borghese 81
Boss, Hugo 78
Boucheron 120, 122
Boudoir 129
Bourdon, Pierre 46, 77, 132
Bourgeois, Bernard 43
Brosius, Christopher 99
Brosseau, Jean-Charles 43
Brown, Bobbi 88
Bulgari 94, 134
Bulgari Eau Parfumée & Extrême 94
Burnham, Arthur 45
Busse, Betty 60
Buxton, Mark 133
By 35
Byblos 84

Cabochard 114
Cacharel 28, 31, 80, 122
Cain, Claire 88
Calandre 47
Calèche 106
Calyx 76
Carles, Jean 107, 119, 129
Carolina Herrera 62, 89
Caron 58, 115, 121, 133
Caron, Françoise 83
Cartier 82, 140

Carven 107
Cašmir 123
Catapano, Josephine 22
Cavalier, Jacques
  floral family 29, 32, 34, 38, 62
  fruity family 83
  oriental family 128
Cellier, Germaine 22, 59, 113, 114
Cerruti 88
Chaillan, Raymond 28
Chakra V 96
Chamade 46
Champs-Elysées 39
Chanel
  chypre family 102, 115
  floral family 37, 48, 50
  No5 48
  No19 102
  oriental family 131
Chanel, Coco 102, 131
Chant, Bernard 31, 114
Chapuis, Anne Sophie 99
Charlie 108
Cheap and Chic 36
Chloë 60, 75
Chloë Innocence 75
Chopard 123
chypre family 14, 16, 101—15
  animal 112—13
  floral 108
  fruity 109—11
  green 102—4
  leather 113—15
  pure 106—7
  woody 104—5
Citrus Paradis 70
cK one 96
Clarins 93
Clinique 79, 103
Coco 131
Cofci 50
Cofinluxe 50
Comme des Garçons 98, 133
Contradiction 34
Cool Water Woman 77
Coriandre 104
Coty, François 64
Coueslant, Yves 27

Coup de Fouet 133
Coupy, Gérard 137
Courtiére, Jean 119
Courtin-Clarins, Jacques 93
Couturier, Jacqueline 104
Couturier, Jean 104
Cox, Patrick 41
Créations Aromatiques 74
Creed 42, 72
Creed, Henry 42
Creed, Olivier 72
Cresp, Olivier 31, 110, 127
Cristalle 102
Crown Perfumery 41
Cuir de Russie 115
Czech & Speake 70

D&G Feminine 36
Dali 50
Dali, Salvadore 50
Daltroff, Ernest 58, 115, 121
Dana 129
Davidoff 77
Dazzling Gold and Silver 37
de Chiris, Yves 127
de la Renta, Oscar 35
de Mourgues, Alain 57
de Nicolaï 27
de Nicolaï, Patricia 27
Deci Delà 109
Deléamont, Francis 120
Demeter 99
Desprez, Jean 135
Diener, Jean-Jacques 140
Diesel 82
Diesel Plus Plus Feminine 82
Dinand, Pierre 130, 137
Dior, Christian
  chypre family 103, 113
  floral family 24, 46, 57
  herbaceous family 95
  oriental family 124, 131, 134
Diorella 103
Diorissimo 24
Diptyque 27, 73
Dir, Claude 88
Dirt 99
Diva 108
Dolce & Gabbana 35, 36, 125
Dolce Vita 46

D'Orsay 93
Doyen, Isabelle 92
drydown 16, 18—19
Dune 134

Eau de Charlotte 39
eau de Cologne 16, 71, 97
Eau de Cologne Impériale 71
Eau de Lavande 92
eau de parfum 10, 16
eau de toilette 10, 11, 16
Eau d'Eté 27
Eau d'Hadrien 70
Eau Dynamisante 93
eau fraîche 16
Eau Sauvage 95
Eden 80
Elléna, Jean-Claude 29, 94
English Lavender 90
Envy 60
Ermenidis, Illias 84
Escada 66
Escape 77
Eternity 23
Etiquette Bleue 93
Etro 26

Fabron, Francis 51, 54
Farina, Jean-Marie 97
Feminis family 97
Feminité du Bois 132
Femme 110
Fendi 126
ferny scents see herbaceous
    family
Ferragamo Pour Femme 29
Ferragamo, Salvatore 29
Ferre, Gianfranco 61
Fidji 22
Firmenich 33, 35, 74, 137
First 29
Flechier, Edouard 124
Fleur de Rocaille Classique 58
Fleurs de Bulgarie 42
Flipo, Anne 53
Flirt 80
floral family 12, 21—67
    aldehydic 12, 46—52
    aqueous 12, 32—7
    chypre 108
    fresh 12, 26—31
    fruity 35—41
    green 12, 22—5
    mood impact 8—9

oriental 118—21
powdery 12, 42—3
pure 12, 53—8
rich 12, 65—7
sexual signals 8
sweet 12, 58—64
woody 12, 44—6
Florasynth 44, 58, 108
Floris 72
Ford, Tom 60, 128
fougère scents see herbaceous
    family
Fracas 59
Fragile 62
Fragonard 26
Fraysse, André 49
Frémont, Harry 79
French Lime Blossom 30
fruity family 12, 69—85
    aqueous 73—81
    chypre 109—11
    citrus 70—2
    exotic 84—5
    floral 35—41
    herbaceous 89
    oriental 121—5
    sweet 82—4
Fuchs, Georges 26

Galliano, John 61, 118, 131
Garouste & Bonetti 109
Gaultier, Jean-Paul 38, 62
Gavary, Max 64
Ghost 126
Gianfranco Ferre 61
Giò 83
Giorgio 58
Giorgio of Beverly Hills 58
Giraux, Pascal 41
Givenchy 51, 64, 118, 119
glossary 18—19
Gonnon, Robert 28
Gonon, René 71
Gottlieb, Ann 96, 138
Goutal, Annick 39, 70, 92
Graham, Florence 26
Gras, Martin 129
green scents 12, 16, 22—5,
    70—2, 92—7
Grès 114
Grojsman, Sophia
    chypre family 109
    floral family 23, 40, 57
    fruity family 76

oriental family 122
Gucci 60, 128
Guerlain
    chypre family 111
    floral family 24, 39, 46, 65
    fruity family 71
    herbaceous family 91
    oriental family 135, 136,
        139
Guerlain, Aimé 91
Guerlain, Jacques 24, 65, 91,
    111, 136, 139
Guerlain, Jean-Paul 39, 46,
    135
Guerlain, Pierre Francois-
    Pascal 71
Guichard, Jean 80, 109, 122,
    138

Haarman & Reimer 133
Habanita 140
Halston 105
Happy 79
heart notes 16
Heliotrope 26
Helleu, Jacques 108
herbaceous family 12, 14,
    87—99
    airy/earthy 99
    aqueous 88—9
    citrus 92—7
    fruity 89
    semi-oriental 91—2
    spicy 98
Hermès 43, 106
Herpin, Richard 67
Herrera, Carolina 62, 89
High 41
Hilfiger, Tommy 81
Houbigant 53
Hugo Woman 78
Hypnotic Poison 131

Iceberg 78
Iceberg Twice 78
IFF (International Flavours &
    Fragrances) 35, 36, 40,
    103, 125
Il Bacio 81
Indiscret 38
Irebe, Paul 49
Isabell, Robert 55
Ivoire 44
J'adore 57

Jaïpur 122
Je Reviens 52
Jean-Paul Gaultier 38, 62
Jicky 91
Jolie Madame 113
Joop! 74
Joop, Wolfgang 74
Joy 56
Jungle 85

Kaiser, Roman 55
Kawakubo, Rei 133
Kedeo, Jean 45, 66, 85
Keller, Helen 7
Kenzo 33, 85
Klein, Calvin 23, 34, 77, 96,
    138
Knowing 106
Knox Leet, Desmond 27, 73
Koichi 96

La Perla 105
Labbe, Sophie 118
Lagerfeld, Karl 58, 60
L'Air du Temps 54
Lalique 64
Lalique, Marc 54
Lalique, René 52, 64, 140
Lancôme 40, 71, 79, 83, 137
Lanvin, Jeanne 49
Laporte, Jean 73
Laporte, Jean Francois 30
Laroche, Guy 22
L'Artisan 53, 73
Lauder, Estée 88, 96, 103
    chypre family 106
    floral family 33, 37, 44, 61
    oriental family 132
Lauren, Ralph 23, 75
Le Feu d'Issey 128
L'Eau d'Issey 32
Leget, Paul 28
Lei 98
Lelong, Lucien 38
Ley, Margaretha 66
L'Heure Bleue 65
Lightfoot Schultz, William 98
Lily of the Valley 25
L'Interdit 51
L'Ombre dans L'Eau 27
Lorson, Natalie 75
Louit, Annette 28
Loulou 122
Lutens, Serge 132, 138

Ma Griffe 107
Madame Rochas 51
Magie Noire 137
Maître Parfumeur et Gantier 30
Malone, Jo 30
Mane 38, 75, 77
Mansau, Serge 33, 41, 112
Marbert 82
Mary, Jean-Pierre 122
Masotti, Ada 105
Mateu, Rosendo 95
Mathieu, Christiane 33
Matton, Cecile 84
Matts, Roy 79
Maxwell, Elsa 56
McCartney, Stella 75
McQueen, Alexander 118
Menardo, Annick 131, 134
Messina, Joe 60
Michael H. 47
mid-notes 16
Mimosa pour moi 53
Miss Dior 113
Mitsouko 111
Miyake, Issey 32, 128
Molinard 140
Molinard and Roure 140
Monod, Véronique 124
Montana, Claude 112
Montana Parfum de Peau 112
mood-altering aromas 8–9
Morillas, Alberto 96
Morsetti, Michael 58
Moschino, Franco 36, 137
Muelhens 97
Mugler, Thierry 127
Mûre et Musc 73
Must de Cartier 140

Nagel, Christina 126
Narcisse Noir 121
Neroli Sauvage 72
Niki de Saint Phalle 104
Noa 31
Normandie 42

Ô de Lancôme 71
Ô Oui 79
Obsession 138
Odeur 53, 99
Old Spice 98
Ombre Rose 43

Opium 130
Organza 118
oriental family 14, 16, 116–40
  amber 136–9
  animal 140
  floral 118–21
  fruity 121–5
  gourmand 125–8
  herbaceous 91–2
  smoky 134
  spicy 129–33
  woody balsamic 135–6

Paco 95
Pakzad, Bijan 65
Pallix, Martine 99
Paloma Picasso 112
Parfum d'été 33
Paris 57
Patou, Jean 42, 45, 56, 66
Paul Smith Women 45
Pellegrino, Roger 28
Penhaligon 24
Peretti, Elsa 105
perfume
  choosing 9–10, 12–14
  concentrations 10, 16
  entry description 14–15
  families 12
  reasons for wearing 7–9
  rules for wearing 11
  storage 11
perfume house 14
perfumer 14–15
Philosykos 73
Picasso, Paloma 112
Pickles, Sheila 25
Piguet, Robert 59, 114
Pleasures 33
Poême 83
Poison 124
Polge, Jacques 37, 102, 108, 121, 131
Polo Sport Woman 75
powdery scents 12, 42–3
Prescriptives 76, 80
Puig, Antonio 89
pure parfum 10, 16
Python 123

Quelques Fleurs L'Original 53
Rabanne, Paco 34, 47, 95
Rateau, Armand-Albert 49

Rechelbacher, Horst 96
Revlon 108
Revson, Charles 108
Ricci, Nina 54, 109
Rive Gauche 47
Robert, Guy 51, 106
Robert, Henri 102
Robertet 26
Rochas, Marcel 51, 110
Roche, Daniele 98, 118
Roger et Gallet 97
Roger, Maurice 46, 124
Roos, Chantal 32
Ropion, Dominique 23, 64, 85, 119
Roucel, Maurice 60
Roudnitska, Edmond 24, 95, 103, 110
Roure, Givaudan
  floral family 34, 43, 55, 59, 63, 65
  fruity family 81, 82
  oriental family 123, 140
Route du Thé 89
Rush 128
Rykiel, Sonia 125

Safari 23
Saint Laurent, Yves 47, 57, 84, 109, 130
Saint Phalle, Niki de 104
Samsara 135
Sarne, Tanya 126
Schiaparelli, Elsa 119
Secrete Datura 30
Serra, Javier 129
sex 8, 10, 11
Shalimar 139
Sheldrake, Christopher 132, 138
Shiseido 132, 138
Shocking 119
Shulton 98
Sieuzac, Jean-Louis 51, 85, 125, 130, 134
sillage 11, 19
skin, effects 9, 10, 11
Smell This 90
Smith, Paul 45
So De La Renta 35
So Pretty 82
Sonia Rykiel 125
Special No. 127, 72

spicy scents 98, 129–33
Sublime 66
Süe, Louis 42
Sunflowers 76
synthetics 15, 18, 19

Tabac Blond 115
Tabu 129
Taylor, Elizabeth 63
Theorema 126
Tiare 55
Tiempe Passate 136
Tiffany 121
Tommy Girl 81
top notes 10, 16
Trésor 40
Trussardi 123

Ultraviolet 34
Ungaro, Emanuel 108

Vacher, Paul 113
Valentino 118
Van Cleef 41
Van Cleef & Arpels 29, 41, 67
Vent Vert 22
Versace 63
Very Valentino 118
Voekl, Frank 55
Vol de Nuit 136

Wandel, Ursula 78
Wargnye, Pierre 105
Wertheimer 102
Westwood, Vivienne 129
White Diamonds 63
White Linen 44
woody scents 12, 44–6, 104–5, 135–6
Worth 52

Yamamoto, Yohji 85
Yardley 90
Yohji 85
Youth Dew 132
Ysatis 119
Yves Saint Laurent 47, 57, 84, 109, 130
Yvresse 109

Zed, Madame 49